Lotus Illustrated DICTIONARY of

MECHANICAL ENGINEERING

Lotus PRESS

4263 / 3, Ansari Road,
Daryaganj, New Delhi-02

Lotus *Illustrated*
DICTIONARY
of
MECHANICAL ENGINEERING

© Lotus Press: 2008

ISBN 81 89093 48 7

Published by:
LOTUS PRESS
4263/3, Ansari Road, Daryaganj,
New Delhi-110002
Ph: 32903912, 23280047
E-mail: lotus_press@sify.com
www: lotuspress.co.in

Printed at: **Saras Graphics,** Delhi

PREFACE

This book is for students, professors and engineers - to be read, understood and enjoyed. It is consciously written in a clear, informal and direct style designed to talk to the reader and to gain his or her immediate interest in the challenging and yet beautiful discipline of Mechanical Engineering. The explanation of each term is carefully constructed to make sense to the reader. This book has been developed from the author's experience in teaching Mechanical engineering. Such courses require careful attention to the structure and sequence of the presentation of basic material, and to the manner in which sophisticated subjects are described to the uninitiated reader. The facts presentation is simple and precise. Many of the terms given in the dictionary are supplemented by their pictorial representations. In the past decade the branch of Mechanical Engineering has taken a big leap thanks to the development of computers. With so much of development it is much needed that all the recent developments be taken into considerations. This fact is kept in mind while developing this dictionary. But it has been tried that the subjects are dealt proportionately according to their weightage.

Hope this venture will become the best buddy of the students of Mechanical Engineering and they will enjoy it thoroughly.

■ 1,2,4 pass

the number of times the fluid passed through the tube bundle. In a one pass unit the tube side medium passes through all the tubes once. In a two pass unit it passes through one half of the tubes and returns through the other half. A four pass unit goes through approximately one quarter of the tubes, down and back four times. Greater than 1 Pass is referred to as a multi-pass unit.

■ ablative

describes a material that absorbs heat through a decomposition process called pyrolysis at or near the exposed surface.

■ abnormal failure

an artificially induced failure of a component, usually as a result of "abnormals" testing for regulatory agency safety compliance.

■ abrasion

the displacement and/or detachment of metallic particles from a surface as a consequence of being exposed to flowing solids, fluids or gases.

■ abrasion resistance

degree of resistance of a material to abrasion or wear.

■ abrasion-corrosion

a synergistic process involving both abrasive wear and corrosion,, in which each of these processes is affected by the simultaneous action of the other, and in many cases is thereby accelerated.

■ abrasive wear

1. wear due to hard particles or hard protuberances forced against and moving along a solid surface. 2. the displacement and / or detachment of metallic particles from a surface as a consequence of being exposed to flowing fluids or gases.

■ abrasives

materials for grinding, polishing, blasting, either in loose form or bonded to form wheels, bricks, or files, or applied to paper and cloth by glue or resin. Natural abrasives include emery, corundum, garnet, sand, flint, etc. Metallic shot and grit are also used as abrasives in cleaning castings.

■ abrasivity

the ability of a material or substance to cause abrasive wear.

■ absolute entropy

is entropy calculated relative to the absolute reference point determined by the third law of thermodynamics.

■ absolute impact velocity

see **impact velocity**.

■ **absolute micron rating**

all (not just 98%) particles larger than the stated micron size have been removed from the fluid being filtered.

■ **absolute or specific humidity**

(also called humidity ratio) is the mass of water vapour present in a unit mass of dry air; that is, it is the ratio of the mass of water vapour to the mass of dry air in atmospheric air.

■ **absolute pressure**

is the actual pressure at a given position and it is measured relative to absolute vacuum (i.e., absolute zero pressure). Throughout this text, the pressure P will denote absolute pressure unless specified otherwise.

■ **absorption refrigeration systems**

involve the absorption of a refrigerant by a transport medium. The most widely used absorption refrigeration system is the ammonia-water system, where ammonia (NH_3) serves as the refrigerant and water (H_2O) as the transport medium. Absorption refrigeration systems are economically attractive when there is a source of inexpensive heat energy at a temperature of 100 to 200 °C. Some examples of inexpensive heat energy sources include geothermal energy, solar energy, and waste heat from cogeneration or process steam plants, and even natural gas when it is available at a relatively low price.

■ **Ac1**

the temperature at which austenite begins to form on heating.

■ **Ac3**

in hypoeutectoid steel, the temperature at which transformation of ferrite into austenite is completed upon heating.

■ **acceleration period**

in cavitation and liquid impingement erosion, the stage following the incubation period, during which the erosion rate increases from near zero to a maximum value. (See also **erosion rate-time pattern**.)

■ **accelerator**

chemical additive that hastens cure or chemical reaction.

■ **acceptable runner/cavity ratio**

runner systems designed for high pressure drops to minimise material usage and increase frictional heating in the runner.

■ **accm**

in hypereutectoid steel, the temperature at which cementite goes into complete solution with austenite.

■ **accumulation period**

in cavitation and liquid impingement erosion, a less-preferred term for acceleration period.

■ **accumulator (steam)**

a pressure vessel containing water and/or steam, which is used to store the heat of steam for use at a late period and at some lower pressure.

■ accuracy

the ability of a robot to reach a given point in space repeatedly, and how far off it will be in the worst case.

■ acid

1) a solution or liquid with a pH less than 7. 2) term applied to slags, refractors, and minerals containing a high percentage of silica.

■ acid brittleness (picking brittleness)

lack of ductility induced in steel when it is pickled in dilute acid to remove scale - commonly attributed to the absorption of hydrogen.

■ acid cleaning

the process of cleaning the interior surfaces of steam generating units by filling the unit with dilute acid accompanied by an inhibitor to prevent corrosion, and subsequently draining, washing and neutralising the acid by a further wash of alkaline water.

■ acid embrittlement

embrittlement during pickling due to absorption of hydrogen.

■ acid process

a steel making method using an acid refractory-lined (usually silica) furnace. Neither sulphur or phosphorus is removed.

■ acidity

represents the amount of free carbon dioxide, mineral acids and salts (especially sulphates of iron and aluminium) which hydrolyse to give hydrogen ions in water and is reported as milliequivalents per litre of acid, or ppm acidity as calcium carbonate, or pH the measure of hydrogen ions concentration.

■ actuator

an *actuator* converts a link signal into force/torque or motion signals.

You can configure a *body actuator* to apply forces/torques to a body either as an explicit function of time or through feedback forces/torques.

You can configure a *joint actuator* to apply forces/torques between the bodies connected on either side of the joint.

You can configure a *driver actuator* to apply relative motion between the bodies connected on either side of the driver.

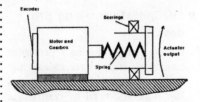

■ adaptive investment casting process

a lost wax process employing one of three methods; centrifugal, vacuum or gravity-pouring casting.

■ adaptive behaviour

the means by which agents cope with a changing world using a spectrum of machines, learning techniques including reinforcement learning, neural networks, fuzzy logic and evolutionary computing.

adaptive interfaces

a mode of interaction between human and computer that changes ('adapts') to fit the current situation. Adaptive interfaces typically involve online processing of sensor information to optimise the way data are displayed and the way user commands are interpreted.

addition

polymerisation reaction in which no byproducts are formed.

addition agent

1. any material added to a charge of molten metal in bath or ladle to bring alloy to specifications
2. reagent added to plating bath.

additives

ingredients mixed into resin to improve properties.

adeline steelmaking process

method of producing a precision casting of steel or steel alloys using aluminolthermic process and lost wax, followed by centrifugal action.

adhesive

substance applied to mating surfaces, to bound them together by surface attachment.

adhesive wear

wear due to localised bonding between contacting solid surfaces leading to material transfer between the two surfaces or loss from either surface.

adiabatic compression

a type of compression where no heat is transferred to or from the gas during the compression process

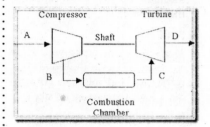

adiabatic flame temperature

the theoretical temperature that would be attained by the products of combustion provided the entire chemical energy of the fuel, the sensible heat content of the fuel and combustion above the datum temperature, were transferred to the products of combustion. This assumes: No heat loss to surroundings and no dissociation.

adiabatic process

is a process during which there is no heat transfer. The word adiabatic comes from the Greek word *adiabatos*, which means not to be passed.

Adiabatic Process

Adiabatic Expansion or compression of an ideal gas:

$$PV_i^\gamma = P_fV_f^\gamma$$

$$\gamma = \frac{c_P}{c_V}$$

■ **adiabatic saturation process**

is the process in which a steady stream of unsaturated air of unknown specific humidity is passed through a long insulated channel that contains a pool of water. As the air flows over the water, some water will evaporate and mix with the airstream. The moisture content of air will increase during this process, and its temperature will decrease, since part of the latent heat of vapourisation of the water that evaporates will come from the air. If the channel is long enough, the airstream will exit as saturated air (100 percent relative humidity) at the exit temperature.

■ **adiabatic saturation temperature**

is the exit temperature that air attains in the adiabatic saturation process.

■ **adjoining CS**

the *adjoining CS* of a Body CS is the CS on the neighbouring body or ground directly connected to the original Body CS by a Joint, Constraint, or Driver.

■ **adsorbent filter**

a filter medium primarily intended to hold soluble and insoluble contaminants on its surface by molecular adhesion.

■ **Aecm, Ae1, and Ae3**

equilibrium transformation temperatures in steel.

■ **aeration**

making contact between air and a liquid by spraying liquid into the air or by agitating the liquid to promote absorption of air. Also act of fluffing, moulding sand.

■ **AFS tests**

a number of standard tests to evaluate moulding and core sands.

■ **afterburner**

is a section added between the turbine and the nozzle of an aircraft turbine engine where additional fuel is injected into the oxygen-rich combustion gases leaving the turbine. As a result of this added energy, the exhaust gases leave at a higher velocity, providing extra thrust for short takeoffs or combat conditions.

■ **age hardening**

hardening by aging, usually after rapid cooling or cold working.

■ **aging**

a change in properties of metals and alloys which occurs slowly at room temperature and will proceed rapidly at higher temperatures. The change in properties is often, but not always, due to a phase change (precipitation), but never involves a change in chemical composition of the metal or alloy.

■ **air**

the mixture of oxygen, nitrogen, and other gases, which with varying amounts of water vapour, forms the atmosphere of the earth.

■ **air atomising oil burner**

a burner for firing oil in which the

oil is atomised by compressed air, which is forced into and through one or more streams of oil which results in the breaking of the oil into a fine spray.

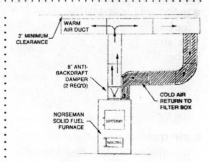

air conditioners

are refrigerators whose refrigerated space is a room or a building instead of the food compartment.

air consumption

pneumatic and electro-pneumatic positioners require a high quantity of intrinsic air also in fixed position, smart positioners with Piezo valves require air only when the valve position has to be changed.

air curtain

a component of a compressed air line that provides wide are a coverage with a thin sheet of air. Also amplifies compressed air flow, reduces noise. Used in blowing, cooling. Also known as air knife.

air cylinder

computer-type logic calculations accomplished by small air valves.

air deficiency

insufficient air, in an air-fuel mixture, to supply the oxygen required for complete oxidation of the fuel.

air furnace

reverbatory-type furnace in which metal is melted by heat from fuel burning at one end of the hearth, passing over the bath toward the stack at the other end. Heat also is reflected from the roof and side walls.

air infiltration

the leakage of air into a setting or duct.

air motor

a device with a shaft that will turn when pressurised air is applied.

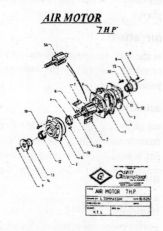

AIR MOTOR
7 H P

air preheater

a heat exchanger, which heats combustion air.

air pump

a pump which is used to deliver air to the aquarium. The pump pushes air through silicon tubing and to air stones or other aquatic decor. They are also an essential for UGF's (undergravel filters). An air stone is placed in each clear tube. When the air bubbles travel upward, they generate steady current which brings water from the bottom, through the tubes and to the surface.

■ air quality

pneumatic positioners are relatively insensitive, in contrast electro-pneumatic positioners are sensitive to oil, dust and water, smart positioners require a higher air quality.

■ air quenching

accelerated cooling of alloy in an air stream from temperatures above the Ac3 temperature.

■ air scale

scale left on ferrous metal in processing, usually from heating in presence of air.

■ air shaft

an air borne device that is used to maintain rolls of wounded strips on a shaft.

■ air vent

a valved opening in the top of the highest drum of a boiler or pressure vessel for venting air.

■ air whistle

a whistle intended for operation on compressed air only. In railroad practice the name is often given to a cab signal or peanut whistle, to distinguish it from the steam whistle mounted on the boiler.

■ air, saturated

air which contains the maximum amount of water vapour that it can hold at its temperature and pressure.

■ airblasting

a cleaning operation, as cleaning sand from moulds.

■ air-free

the descriptive characteristic of a substance from which air has been removed.

■ air-fuel ratio

is a frequently used quantity in the analysis of combustion processes to quantify the amounts of fuel and air. It is usually expressed on a mass basis and is defined as the ratio of the mass of air to the mass of fuel for a combustion process.

■ air-hardening steel

a steel containing sufficient alloy to fully harden during cooling in air. Typically this term is restricted to steels being able to harden in sections of about 2 in. (51 mm) or more.

■ air-source heat pumps

use the cold outside air as the heat source in winter.

■ air-standard assumptions

reduce the analysis of gas power cycles to a manageable level by utilising the following approximations:
1. The working fluid is air, which continuously circulates in a closed loop and always behaves as an ideal gas.
2. All the processes that make up the cycle are internally reversible.

3. The combustion process is replaced by a heat-addition process from an external source.

4. The exhaust process is replaced by a heat rejection process that restores the working fluid to its initial state.

■ **air-standard cycle**

is a cycle for which the air-standard assumptions are applicable.

■ **alarm**

a suitable horn, bell, light or other device which when operated will give notice of malfunction or off normal condition.

■ **algorithm**

a set of procedures used to solve a problem.

■ **alkaline derusting**

an electrical process for derusting steel, cast iron and other ferrous alloys without using heat.

■ **alkalinity**

represents the amount of carbonates, bicarbonates, hydroxides and silicates or phosphates in the water and is reported as grains per gallon, or ppm as calcium carbonate.

■ **allowable working pressure**

see **design pressure**.

■ **allowance (tolerance)**

in a foundry, the clearance specified; difference in limiting sizes, as minimum clearance or maximum interference between mating parts, as computed arithmetically.

■ **alloy**

a substance having metallic prop-

erties and composed of two or more chemical elements of which at least one is metal. Usually possesses qualities different from those of the components.

■ **alloy steel**

steel containing significant quantities of alloying elements other than carbon and the commonly accepted amounts of manganese, silicon, sulphur, and phosphorus.

■ **alpha - ferrite**

body-centred cubic type of pure iron, stable below 1670 °F (910 °C).

■ **alpha martensite**

a form or stage of martensite of somewhat arbitrary distinction, probably representing the least developed and most distorted stage in the transformation of austenite to martensite at ordinary temperatures.

■ **alpha process**

a shell moulding and core-making method in which a thin resin-bonded shell is baked with a less expensive, highly permeable material.

■ **alternating stress**

stress produced in a material by forces acting alternating in opposite directions.

■ **Amagat's law of additive volumes**

the volume of a gas mixture is equal to the sum of the volumes each gas would occupy if it existed alone at the mixture temperature and pressure.

■ ambient air

the air that surrounds the equipment. The standard ambient air for performance calculations is air at 80 °F, 60% relative humidity, and a barometric pressure of 29.921 in. Hg, giving a specific humidity of 0.013 lb of water vapour per lb of dry air.

■ ambient temperature

the temperature of the air surrounding the equipment.

■ Ames portable hardness tester

the Rockwell penetration method of testing hardness of metals can be made with this tester by applying pressure to the penetrator by screw action.

■ amorphous

non-crystalline. Material assumes more random molecular structure when cooling.

■ analog

in electronics, a signal that gives information by a change in either its current or its voltage.

■ analysis

quantitative determination of the constituent parts.

■ analysis line

in spectrographic analysis, the particular spectral line used in determining the concentration of an element.

■ analysis, ultimate

chemical analysis of solid, liquid or gaseous fuels. In the case of coal or coke, determination of carbon, hydrogen, sulphur, nitrogen, oxygen, and ash.

■ angle of attack

in impingement erosion, the angle between the direction of motion of an impinging liquid or solid particle and the tangent to the surface at the point of impact.

■ angle of incidence

in impingement erosion, the angle between the direction of motion of an impinging liquid or solid particle and the normal to the surface at the point of impact.

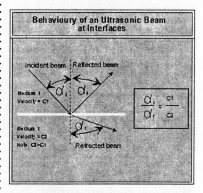

■ angle testing

a method of ultrasonic testing using shear waves introduced from the surface of the material at approximately 45 degrees.

■ angle-ply laminate

any balanced laminate consisting of plies at angles of plus and minus theta, where theta is an acute angle with the principal laminate axis.

■ anisotropic

not isotropic. Exhibiting different

properties when tested along axes in different directions within the material.

■ anisotropy

the characteristic of exhibiting different property values in different directions with respect to a fixed reference system in the material.

■ annealing

heating to and holding at a suitable temperature, followed by cooling at a suitable rate to lower the hardness or alter other mechanical or physical properties.

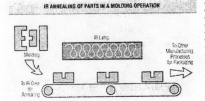

■ annual fuel utilisation efficiency

accounts for the combustion efficiency as well as other losses such as heat losses to unheated areas and start-up and cool-down losses in buildings.

■ annular

occurs at high gas rates and relatively high liquid rates, it consists of an annulus of liquid coating the wall of the pipe and central core of gas flow; liquid droplets are entrained in the gas.

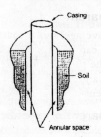

■ anthropomorphic

manlike.

■ anthropopathic robots

robots that can foster and maintain emotional relationships with human beings. Such robots not only perceive and respond to human emotion, but also are possessed of an intrinsic emotional system modeled after human beings. For these robots, emotional state is not merely an outward expression, but rather permeates their control architecture and influences their behaviour.

■ anticarburising compounds

compounds applied to metallic surfaces to prevent surface carbonisation.

■ AOD

see **Argon Oxygen Decarburisation**.

■ APFIM

abbreviation for Atomic Probe Field Ion Microscopy An analytical technique in which atoms are ionised by an electric field near a sharp specimen tip. The field then forces the ions to a fluorescent screen which shows an enlarged image of the tip and individual atoms are made visible.

■ apparent

(or average) molar mass of a mixture can be expressed as the sum of the products of the mole fraction and molar mass of each component in the mixture.

■ apparent area of contact

in tribology, the area of contact between two solid surfaces defined by the boundaries of their macroscopic interface. (Contrast with real area of contact.)

■ apparent contraction

the net contraction of a casting dimension due to true metal contraction, mould wall movement and restraint during solidification and cooling.

■ aquastat

water limit temperature control, a safety device often used on boilers.

■ aramid

aromatic polyamide fibres.

■ arc cutting

using an electric arc to cut metal.

■ arc welding

the process of joining metal together by applying electric current through a protruding wire, melting the pieces and the wire together.

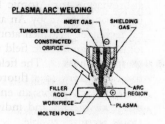

PLASMA ARC WELDING

INERT GAS — SHIELDING GAS
TUNGSTEN ELECTRODE —
CONSTRICTED ORIFICE —
FILLER ROD —
WORKPIECE —
MOLTEN POOL —
ARC REGION
PLASMA

■ arcair torch

an electric arc torch with air ducts running parallel to the electrode, used to remove metal and surface defects from ferrous castings.

■ arca-vena

valve calculation programme to determine Kvs values, nominal diameters and technical design incl. calculation of flow velocity, noise level, control forces etc.

■ arch

the overhead (usually flat) portion of the radiant firebox.

■ ard process

a refinement of the precision casting process, using plastic patterns produced in automatic injection machines.

■ areal weight

weight of a fibre reinforcement per unit area (width times length) of tape or fabric.

■ argon oxygen decarburisation (AOD)

a secondary refining process in which argon, oxygen and nitrogen are injected into a molten bath of steel. The AOD process improves metal cleanliness and thus gives superior mechanical properties.

■ arm

the part of the robot that positions the end-effector and sensors to do their pre-programmed business. Robot arms come in all shapes and sizes. Many (but not all) resemble human arms, and have shoulders, elbows, wrists, even fingers. These are commonly referred to as "jointed-arm" robots.

■ Arnold's fatigue test

(after John Arnold, Brit. Met.), a test for fractures using 850 cyclic stress reverses per min., recording the number of cycles required to produce fracture.

■ arrester

a device to impede the flow of large dust particles or sparks from a stack, usually screening at the top.

■ artifical aging

an aging treatment above room temperature.

■ artificial intelligence

the ability of computers to 'think' in ways similar to human beings. Examples might be reasoning, adaptation, decision making, and learning from mistakes. At present, artificial intelligence has a long way to go before machines can be considered truly 'smart.' Present day 'AI' does allow machines to mimic certain simple human thought processes, but can't begin to match the quickness and complexity of the brain.

■ artificial life

a human made object that has the essential qualities of living things: the ability to reproduce itself, consciousness, etc. To this date, no proven forms of artificial life have been created- what exactly constitutes 'living' versus 'non living' is the subject of much debate, on both technological and philosophical fronts.

■ artificially balanced runner system

balancing a runner system by adjusting the pressure drop of a long large diameter runner against a short small diameter runner. Since pressure drop over the small diameter runner will be much more affected by heat loss than the large diameter runner, an artificially balanced runner system will work with a set range of moulding conditions. The width of this range of moulding conditions determines the stability of the moulding.

■ AS cast

referring to metal which has not received finishing (beyond gate removal or sandblasting) or treatment of any kind including heat treatment after casting. Similarly, as drawn, as forged and as rolled. (See **Finishing**).

■ AS-fired fuel

fuel in the condition as fed to the fuel burning equipment.

■ ash

the incombustible inorganic matter in the fuel.

■ ash pit

a pit or hopper located below a furnace where refuse is accumulated and from which refuse is removed at intervals.

■ ash-free basis

the method of reporting fuel analysis, whereby ash is deducted and other constituents are recalculated to total 100%.

Asimov's 3 laws of robotics

first published in a 1942 short story by Isaac Asimov (b 1920-d.1992), the 3 laws of robotics are intended to give humanity an ethical framework for the time when intelligent robots become a part of our daily lives.

The laws are:

1. A robot must not injure, or allow the injury of, any human being.

2. A robot must obey all orders from humans, except orders that would contradict the first law.

3. A robot must protect itself, except when to do so would contradict the First or Second Law.

Although they were first proposed in the 1942, they are still regarded as a useful framework to follow. However, they are not official laws, and people have proposed creating robots that might violate them, such as robotic soldiers, or robots that would be expendable in hazardous conditions. The 3 laws help us ask ethical questions about the future of robotics.

aspect ratio

ratio of length to diameter of a fibre.

asperity

in tribology, a protuberance in the small-scale topographical irregularities of a solid surface.

aspirating burner

a burner in which the fuel in a gaseous or finely divided form is burned in suspension, the air for combustion being supplied by bringing into contact with the fuel air drawn through one or more openings, by the lower static pressure created by the velocity of the fuel stream.

AS-received fuel

fuel in the condition as received at the plant.

assembled joint

restricts the Body coordinate systems (CSs) on the two bodies at either end of the joint.

For an *assembled prismatic joint*, the two Body CS origins must lie along the prismatic axis. The two Bodies translate relatively along the same axis.

For an assembled joint with multiple prismatic primitives, the two Body CS origins must lie in the plane or space defined by the directions of the prismatic axes.

For an *assembled revolute joint*, the two Body CS origins must be collocated. The two Bodies rotate relatively about the same axis.

For an assembled joint with multiple revolute primitives, the two Body CS origins must be collocated.

For an *assembled spherical joint*, the two Body CS origins must be collocated at the spherical primitive's pivot point. The two Bodies pivot relatively about this common origin.

You specify an *assembly tolerance* for assembled joints, the maximum dislocation distance allowed between all pairs of assembled Body CS origins and the maximum angle of misalignment between all pairs of assembled Body motion axes. If the distance dislocations and/

or axis misalignments in an assembled joint grow larger than the assembly tolerance, the simulation stops with an error.

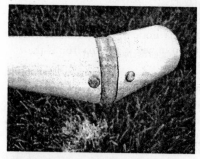

■ **assembly tolerance**

determines how closely an *assembled joint* must be collocated and aligned. An *assembled joint* is connected on either side to Body coordinate systems (CSs) on two Bodies and restricts the relative configurations and motions of those Body CSs.

The assembly tolerances set the *maximum dislocation* of Body CS origins and *maximum misalignment* of motion axes allowed in assembled joints during the simulation.

For *assembled prismatic primitives*, each pair of Body CS origins must lie in the subspace defined by the prismatic axis(es). Each pair of Bodies translates along this (these) common axis(es).

For *assembled revolute primitives*, each pair of Body CS origins must be collocated and their respective rotational axes aligned. Each pair of Bodies rotates about this (these) common axis(es).

For an *assembled spherical primitive*, the pair of Body CS origins must

be collocated. The two Bodies pivot about this common origin. If the two Body CSs separate or the joint axes misalign in a way that makes their connecting assembled joint primitives no longer respect the assembly tolerances, the simulation stops with an error.

■ **A-stage**

an early stage of Polymerisation of thermosetting resins in which the material is still soluble in certain liquids and fusible. (See also **B-stage, C-stage**.)

■ **astronaut**

a person who leaves Earth's atmosphere for the purpose of exploration and research.

■ **atmosphere, furnace**

gases with which metal is in contact during melting or heat treatment.

■ **atmosphere, neutral**

furnace atmosphere which is neither oxidising nor reducing can be made up of an inert gas e.g. argon, or the products of combustion.

■ **atmosphere, oxidising**

furnace atmosphere which gives off oxygen under certain conditions or where there is an excess of oxygen in the product of combustion, or the products of combustion are oxidising to the metal being heated.

■ **atmosphere, reducing**

furnace atmosphere which absorbs oxygen under suitable conditions or in which there is insufficient air to completely burn the fuel, or the product of combustion is reducing to the metal being heated.

■ **atmospheric air**

is the air in the atmosphere, which normally contains some water vapour (or moisture).

■ **atmospheric pressure**

the pressure exerted by the atmosphere. Common units are psi, Pascals (Newtons/meter²), Bars, and Dynes/cm². Atmospheric pressure decreases approximately exponentially with altitude.

Manometers
Open & Closed tube manometers measure pressure.

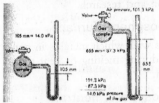

One atmosphere = 760mm of Hg = 101 kPa.
So 1mm of Hg = 0.13 kPa.

■ **atomiser**

a device by means of which a liquid is reduced to a very fine spray.

■ **attenuation period**

in cavitation and liquid impinge-

ment erosion, a less-preferred term for deceleration period.

■ **austenite**

the face-centred-cubic phase of iron and steel, also referred to as gamma iron. In steel, a solid solution in which gamma iron is the solvent.

■ **austenite steel**

any steel containing sufficient alloy to produce a stable austenitic (gamma iron) crystalline structure at ambient temperatures.

■ **autoclave**

closed vessel for applying fluid pressure, with or without heat, to an enclosed object.

■ **autoclave moulding**

moulding technique in which an entire assembly (lay up and tooling) is placed into an autoclave and subjected to heat and elevated pressure for consolidation and/or curing while removing entrapped air and volatiles.

■ **autoignition**

is the premature ignition of the fuel, produces an audible noise which is called engine knock.

■ **automated**

assisted or run with the help of a machine and/or computer.

■ **automated tape laying**

fabrication process in which prepreg material, typically unidirectional tape, is laid across the surface of a mould in multiple layers and directions by an automated tape-application machine to form a structure.

availability factor

the fraction of time during which the unit is in operable condition.

available draft

the draft which may be utilised to cause the flow of air for combustion or the flow of products of combustion.

average

(or apparent) gas constant of a mixture is the universal gas constant divided by the apparent molar mass of the mixture.

average erosion rate

a less preferred term for cumulative erosion rate.

axial fan

consists of a propeller or disc type of wheel within a cylinder that discharges air parallel to the axis of the wheel.

axial winding

filament winding wherein the filaments are parallel, or at a small angle, to the axis of rotation.

axis- in robotics

an individual component free to move relative to the other components.

axis-angle rotation

a representation of a three-dimensional spherical rotation as a rotation axis vector n = (n_x, n_y, n_z) of unit length ($n*n = n_x^2 + n_y^2 + n_z^2 = 1$) and a rotation angle è. Define the rotation axis by the vector n; rotate about that axis by è using the right-hand rule.

The rotation axis direction is equivalent to specifying two independent angles; è is the third independent angle making up the rotation.

In VRML, you represent body rotations by a vector signal [n_x n_y n_z è].

back pressure

the pressure on the upstream side of a valve seat.

back work ratio

is the ratio of the compressor work to the turbine work in gas-turbine power plants.

backflow

the melt flows back out of the mould, returning to the runners.

backing board (backing plate)

a second bottom board on which moulds are opened.

baffle

a plate or wall for deflecting gases or liquids.

■ **baffle cut**

at ITT Standard either 20%, 35%, or 45% of free area or percent of area cut off of the whole diameter baffle plate.

■ **baffle plate**

also called support plate. A plate in which the tubes pass through for support. Also provides a blocked path for the shellside medium. This blocked path forces the shellside medium across the tubes providing better heat exchanger performance.

■ **baffle spacing**

the space in-between the baffle plates on a tube bundle. Baffle spacing is adjusted to achieve maximum heat exchanger performance.

■ **baffle tile**

a tile for deflecting gases.

■ **baffle-type collector**

a device in gas paths utilising baffles so arranged as to deflect dust particles out of the gas stream.

■ **bag filter**

a device containing one or more cloth bags for recovering particles from the dust laden gas or air which is blown through it.

■ **bag moulding**

moulding technique in which the composite structure is placed in a rigid mould and covered with a flexible impermeable layer of film and the edges sealed, followed by consolidation and/or curing with pressure applied by vacuum, autoclave, press or inflation of the bag.

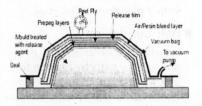

■ **bag-type collector**

a filter in which the cloth filtering medium is made in the form of cylindrical bags.

■ **bainite**

in steel, an acicular aggregate of ferrite and carbide, resulting from an isothermal transformation of austenite at a temperature below the pearlitic range and above Ms.

■ **bake**

heat in an oven to a low controlled temperature to remove gases or to harden a binder.

■ **baked core**

a core which has been heated through sufficient time and temperature to produce the desired physical properties attainable from its oxidising or thermal-setting binders.

■ **baked strength**

compressive, shear, tensile or transverse strength of a mould sand mixture when baked at a temperature above 231°F (111°C) and then cooled to room temperature.

■ balanced laminate

any laminate that contains one ply of minus theta orientation with respect to the principal axis of the laminate for every identical ply with a plus theta orientation.

■ ball burnishing

a method of obtaining a high luster on small parts by rotating them in a wooden-lined barrel with water, burnishing soap, and stainless steel shot.

■ ball screw

a device for transforming rotary motion to linear, or vice versa,

incorporating a threaded rod portion and a nut consisting of a cage holding many ball bearings.

■ band, inside

a loose steel frame placed inside a removable flask to reinforce the sand at the parting line after the flask has been removed.

■ bar

is the unit of pressure equal to 10^5 pascal.

■ bark

the decarburised layer just beneath the scale resulting from heating steel in an oxidising atmosphere.

■ barometer

is a device that measures the atmospheric pressure; thus, the atmospheric pressure is often referred to as the barometric pressure.

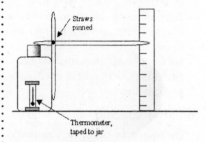

■ barometric pressure

atmospheric pressure as determined by a barometer usually expressed in inches of mercury.

■ bars (cleats)

ribs of metal or wood placed across the flask to help support the sand in the cope.

■ base

the platform which supports the manipulator arm.

■ base (base body)

the point from which the joint is directed. The joint directionality runs from base to follower body. Joint directionality sets the direction and the positive sign of all joint position/angle, motion, and force/torque data.

■ base load

base load is the term applied to

that portion of a station or boiler load that is practically constant for long periods.

base plate

a plate to which the pattern assemblies are attached and to which a flask is subsequently attached to form the mould container.

basket weave

woven reinforcement where two or more warp threads go over and under two or more filling threads in a repeat pattern; less stable than the plain weave but produces a flatter, stronger, more pliable fabric.

batch

material made by the same process at the same time having identical characteristics throughout. Same as lot.

batch oven

oven use to bake a number of cores at one time.

bath

molten metal on the hearth of a furnace, in a crucible, or in a ladle.

batten

a wooden bar or strip fastened to

bottom or follow board for rigidity or to prevent distortion during ramming of the mould.

bead

1) half-round cavity in a mould, or half-round projection or moulding on a casting, 2) a single deposit of weld metal produced by fusion.

beaded tube end

the rounded exposed end of a rolled tube when the tube metal is formed over against the sheet in which the tube is rolled.

beam and sling

tackle used in conjunction with a crane for turning over the cope or drag of a mould prior to assembly.

bearing

supports used to hold a revolving shaft in its proper position.

Beattie-Bridgeman equation of state

is one of the best known and is a reasonably accurate equation of state.

bedding

sinking a pattern down into the sand to the desired position and ramming sand around it.

bedding a core

resting an irregularly shaped core on a bed of sand for drying.

bed-in

method whereby drag may be rammed in the pit or flask without necessity of rolling over. Process used in production of heavy castings.

behaviour

the primitive building blocks for robot control and action. Depending on the control architecture, Behaviour can be either simple stimulus-response pairings or more complex rule based units for carrying out a particular competency. Behaviour can be sequenced or run in parallel to produce higher-level capabilities.

Beilby layer

an altered surface layer of supposedly amorphous material formed on a crystalline solid during mechanical polishing, whose existence was proposed in Sir George Beilby's writings. The existence of such a layer is not supported by recent research, and the use of this term is therefore considered archaic and is strongly discouraged.

bellows

a flexible, thin-walled, circumferencially corrugated cylinder. It may have integral ends and can expand or contract axially under changing pressure.

bellows seal

a seal for the valve stem in which the ends of the sealing material are fastened to bonnet or stem. The material expands and contracts with stem travel.

bench rammer

a short rammer used by bench moulders.

bench-blower

a small core-blowing machine, utilising a removable sand magazine and blow heat.

bending strength

upper limit of normal stress of a beam at which fracture or excessive plastic deformation occurs.

Benedict-Webb-Rubin equation of state

is one of the more recent and very accurate equations of state.

bentonite

a colloidal clay derived from volcanic ash and employed as a binder in connection with synthetic sands, or added to ordinary natural (clay-bonded) sands where extra strength is required.

Bernoulli's equation

is a form of the conservation of momentum principle for steady-flow control volumes.
Choked flow occurs in a nozzle when the mass flow reaches a maximum value for the minimum flow area. This happens when the flow properties are those required to increase the fluid velocity to the velocity of sound at the minimum flow area location.

BHN

Brinell Hardness Number.

bias fabric

fabric in which warp and fill fibres are at an angle to the length.

biaxial fabric

fabric with two non-interwoven

layers: a unidirectional warp (0°) layer and a unidirectional weft (90°) layer which are bonded together, usually by through-the-thickness stitching, to form a single sheet of fabric. (See also **triaxial fabric, quadraxial fabric.**)

■ **biaxial winding**

filament winding wherein helical bands are laid in sequence, side by side, with no fibre crossover.

■ **bi-directional**

a device designed for flow in both directions.

■ **bidirectional laminate**

laminate with fibres oriented in more than one direction on the same plane.

■ **bimetal**

casting, usually centrifugal, made of two different metals fused together.

■ **binary vapour cycle**

is a vapour cycle in which the condenser of the high-temperature cycle (also called the topping cycle) serves as the boiler of the low-temperature cycle (also called the bottoming cycle). That is, the heat output of the high-temperature cycle is used as the heat input to the low-temperature one.

■ **bismaleimide (bmi)**

type of thermoset polyimide that cures by an additional reaction, thus avoiding formation of volatiles. Exhibits temperature capabilities between those of epoxy and polyimide.

■ **bit**

one single piece of computer information, either *on* or *off*, 0 or 1.

■ **black lead**

a natural form of graphite used for sleeking green sand moulds, or applied in a water suspension to skin dried moulds.

■ **blackening scab**

a form of casting defect related to an improper coating rather than to the sand.

■ **blacking carbon**

carbonaceous materials such as plumbago, graphite or powdered coke usually mixed with a binder and frequently carried in suspension in water or other liquid; used as thin facing applied to surfaces of moulds or cores to improved casting finish.

■ **blacking hole**

irregular-shaped surface cavities in a casting containing carbonaceous matter. Caused by spilling off of the blacking from the mould surface.

■ **blacking scab**

a casting defect formed by blacking flaking off due to sand expansion and being retained in or on the surface of the metal.

■ **blasting (blast cleaning)**

a process for cleaning or finishing metal objects by use of an air blast or centrifugal wheel that throws abrasive particles against the surface of the work pieces. Small, irregular particles of steel or iron are used as the abrasive in grit blasting, and steel or iron balls in shot blasting.

bleeder

a defect wherein a casting lacks completeness due to molten metal draining or leaking out of some part of the mould cavity after pouring has stopped.

bleeder cloth

layer of woven or non-woven material, not a part of the composite, that allows excess gas and resin to escape during cure.

bleedout

excess liquid resin appearing at the surface of the composite structure, particularly during filament winding.

blended moulding sands

naturally bonded moulding sands which have been mixed or modified by the supplier to produce desirable properties.

blind flange

a solid platelike fitting that is used to seal the end of a flanged end pipe.

blind nipple

a nipple, or a short piece of pipe or tube, closed at one end.

blister

a shallow blow with a thin film of the metal over it appearing on the surface of a casting.

blocking

adding ferrosilicon or other deoxidising agent to a refined heat to stop all oxidising reactions.

blow holes

1) holes in the head plate or blow plate of a core-blowing machine through which sand is blown from the reservoir into the core box. 2) Irregular shaped cavities with smooth walls produced in a casting when gas is entrapped during mould filling. The gas sources may be air, binder decomposition products or gases dissolved in the molten steel.

blow plate

the plate containing the core sand entrance holes or blow holes used in open-face core boxes.

blowdown

boiler water that is removed from the boiler in order to maintain the desired concentration levels of suspended and dissolved solids in the boiler and removal of sludge.

blowdown valve

a valve generally used to continuously regulate concentration of solids in the boiler, not a drain valve. (Often called continuous blowdown.)

blowdownõ safety valve

the difference between the pressure at which a safety valve opens and at which it closes.

blower

a fan used to force air under pressure.

■ **blower, core or mould**

a device using air pressure to fill a core box or flask with sand.

■ **blowing-off a mould**

cleaning a mould cavity with a stream of compressed air.

■ **blow-off valve**

a specially designed, manually operated, valve that connects to the boiler for the purpose of reducing the concentration of solids in the boiler or for draining purposes. (Often called bottom blowdown.)

■ **blowpipe**

a small pipe or tube through which the breath is blown in removing loose sand from small mould cavities.

■ **blows**

see Blowholes.

■ **bluing**

formation of a thin film of oxide on polished steel to improve its appearance and protect its surface.

■ **bmi**

see bismaleimide.

■ **bob**

a riser or feeder, usually blind, to provide molten metal to the casting during solidification, thereby preventing shrinkage cavities.

■ **body**

the basic element of a mechanical system or machine. It is characterised by.
Its mass properties (mass and inertia tensor)
Its position and orientation in space
Any attached Body coordinate systems

Bodies are connected to one another by joints. Bodies carry no degrees of freedom.

You can attach to a Body block any number of Body coordinate systems (CSs). All Bodies automatically maintain a minimum of one Body CS at the body's centre of gravity (CG). The Body block has special axis triad CS ports, instead of the open, round connector ports O, to indicate the attached Body CSs.

■ **body core**

the main core.

■ **body CS**

a local coordinate system (CS) attached to a body, carried along with that body's motion. In general, bodies accelerate as they move, and therefore Body CSs define non-inertial reference frames. You can attach any number of Body CSs to a Body block, and you can choose where to place the Body CS origins and how to orient the Body CS axes. The Body block has special axis triad CS ports instead of the open, round connector ports, to give you access to these Body CSs for connecting Joint, Sensor, and Actuator blocks.

Every Body block has an automatic, minimum Body CS at its centre of gravity (CG). By default, it also has two other Body CSs for connection to adjacent Joints. The origin and axis orientation of each Body CSs once set by the user during Body configuration, are interpreted as fixed rigidly in that body during the simulation.

■ **boil**

agitation of a bath of metal caused by the liberation of a gas beneath its surface. May be deliberately induced by the addition of oxidising material to a bath containing excess carbon. In the later case it is called a carbon boil and CO or CO_2 are liberated.

■ **boiler**

a closed vessel in which water is heated, steam is generated, steam is superheated, or any combination thereof, under pressure or vacuum by the application of heat from combustible fuels, electricity or nuclear energy.

■ **boiler efficiency**

the term boiler efficiency" is often substituted for combustion or thermal efficiency. True boiler efficiency is the measure of fuel-to-steam efficiency.

■ **boiler horsepower**

the evaporation of 34-1/2 lbs of water per hour from a temperature of 212 °F into dry saturated steam at the same temperature. Equivalent to 33,475 Btu/hr.

■ **boiler rating**

the heating capacity of a boiler expressed in boiler horsepower, Btu/hour, or pounds of steam/hour.

■ **boiler shell**

the outer cylindrical portion of a pressure vessel.

■ **boiler water**

a term construed to mean a representative sample of the circulating boiler water, after the generated steam has been separated and before the incoming feed water or added chemical becomes mixed with it so that its composition is affected.

■ **boiling**

the conversion of a liquid into vapour with the formation of bubbles.

■ **boiling out**

the boiling of highly alkaline water in boiler pressure parts for the removal of oils, greases, etc.

■ **bolt circle**

the circular dimension line on which bolt holes are drilled.

■ **bolted bonnet**

a bonnet which is connected to the neck flange with bolts.

■ **bolted gland**

a device which compresses the stuffing or packing in a stuffing box by means of tightening bolts.

■ **bond**

1) bonding substance or bonding

agents - any material other than water, which, when added to foundry sands, imparts bond strength, 2) the overlapping of brick so as to give both longitudinal and transverse strength.

■ **bond ply**

ply or fabric patch that comes in contact with the honeycomb core during repair.

■ **bond strength**

as measured by load/bond area, the stress required to separate a layer of material from another material to which it is bonded; the amount of adhesion between bonded surfaces.

■ **bonding clay (bonderise)**

any clay suitable for use as a bonding material.

■ **bonnet**

the part of a valve which connects the valve actuator to the body. It may also include the stem packing.

■ **bonnet assembly**

the name of a tube sheet exchanger part. It directs the tubeside medium for distribution through the tubes. It may also contain the tubeside inlet and outlet connections and/or pass ribs. It differs from a channel in the sense that it does not have a removable cover. See Channel Assembly and Waterbox.

■ **bonnet packing**

material used around a stem and within a bonnet to prevent leakage.

■ **bonnetless**

a term used for a pressure seal bonnet.

■ **booster fan**

a device for increasing the pressure or flow of a gas.

■ **bore**

is the diameter of a piston.

■ **boring**

a machining method using single point tools on internal surfaces of revolution.

■ **boron fibre**

fibre produced by chemical vapour deposition of boron onto a core material, usually a tungsten-filament. Because of the deposition process, a boron fibre is of a fairly large diameter, typically about 0.4 mils, and is thus often referred to as a wire.

■ **boss (pad)**

a projection of circular cross-section on a casting. Usually intended for drilling and tapping for attaching parts.

■ **bottom dead centre**

(BDC) is the position of the piston when it forms the largest volume in the cylinder.

■ **bottom running or pouring**

filling of the mould cavity from the bottom by means of gates from the runner.

■ **bottoming cycle**

is a power cycle operating at low average temperatures that receives heat from a power cycle operating at higher average temperatures.

boundary

is the real or imaginary surface that separates the system from its surroundings. The boundary of a system can be *fixed* or *movable*.

boundary work

(*PdV* work) is the work associated with the expansion or compression of a gas in a piston-cylinder device. Boundary work is the area under the process curve on a P-V diagram equal, in magnitude, to the work done during a quasi-equilibrium expansion or compression process of a closed system.

Bourdon tube

named after the French inventor Eugene Bourdon, is a type of commonly used mechanical pressure measurement device which consists of a hollow metal tube bent like a hook whose end is closed and connected to a dial indicator needle.

box

the burners and tubes are enclosed in the heater box, which consists of a structure, refractory lining, and tube supports.

bracket

strengthening strip, rib, or projection on a casting; usually used to prevent hot tearing.

braiding

textile process that intertwines into a pattern three or more strands, yarns or tapes, typically into a tubular shape.

Brayton cycle

was first proposed by George Brayton around 1870. It is used for gas turbines, which operate on an open cycle, where both the compression and expansion processes take place in rotating machinery. The open gas-turbine cycle can be modelled as a closed cycle by utilising the air-standard assumptions. The combustion process is replaced by a constant-pressure heat-addition process from an external source, and the exhaust process is replaced by a constant-pressure heat-rejection process to the ambient air. The ideal Brayton cycle is made up of four internally reversible processes:

1-2 Isentropic compression (in a compressor).
2-3 Constant pressure heat addition.
3-4 Isentropic expansion (in a turbine).
4-1 Constant pressure heat rejection.

Brayton cycle with regeneration

is the Brayton cycle modified with a regenerator, a counterflow heat exchanger, to allow the transfer of heat to the high pressure air leaving the compressor from the high-temperature exhaust gas leaving the turbine.

breakaway (unseating) torque

turning force required to initiate rotation of the closure element of a rotary valve.

breaker ring

an intentionally weak ring within mass of a ring shell mould to be broken by force of casting shrinkage. Prevents hot tear stress.

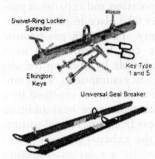

break-in

see run-in.

breakoff notch

a thinner section of a gate or riser to facilitate and ensure clean breaking-off during the cleaning process of casting.

breakout

separation or breakage of fibres when the edges of a composite part are drilled or cut.

breather

loosely woven material that does not come in contact with the resin but serves as a continuous vacuum path over a part in production.

breeching

a duct that transports the products of combustion between parts of a steam generating unit or to the stack.

brittleness

a tendency to fracture without appreciable deformation.

bridge wall temperature

the temperature of the flue gas leaving the radiant section. The term comes from the old horizontal box fired heaters, where a bridge wall physically separated the radiant and convection sections.

bridgewall

a wall in a furnace over which the products of combustion pass.

bright annealing

a process carried out usually in a controlled furnace atmosphere, so surface does not oxidise, remaining bright.

Brinell hardness

the value of hardness of a metal on an arbitrary scale representing kg/mm2, determined by measuring the diameter of the impression made by a ball of given diameter applied under a known load. Values are expressed in Brinell Hardness Numbers, BHN.

brinelling

damage to a solid bearing surface characterised by one or more plastically formed indentations caused by static or impulsive overloads, especially as found in rolling contact bearings. (See also **false brinelling**.)

british thermal unit (btu)

the mean British Thermal Unit is 1/180 of the heat required to raise the temperature of 1 lb of water from 32 °F to 212 °F at a constant atmospheric pressure. A Btu is essentially 252 calories.

■ brittle erosion behaviour

erosion Behaviour having characteristic properties that can be associated with brittle fracture of the exposed surface; i.e., little or no plastic flow occurs, but cracks form that eventually intersect to create erosion fragments.

Notes-In solid impingement an easily observable aspect of erosion helps to distinguish brittle from ductile Behaviour. This is the manner in which volume removal varies with the angle of attack. With brittle erosion the maximum volume, removal occurs at an angle near 90°, in contrast to approximately 25° for ductile erosion Behaviour.

■ brittle fracture

fracture with little or no plastic deformation.

■ broaching

smoothing machined holes or outside surfaces of castings by drawing pushing on or more broaches (special cutting tools) through the roughed out hole.

■ broadgoods

fibres woven into fabrics that may or may not be impregnated with resin; usually furnished in rolls.

■ b-stage

intermediate stage in the Polymerisation reaction of some thermosets in which the material softens with heat and is plastic and fusible but does not entirely dissolve or fuse. The resin of an uncured prepreg or premix is usually in this state. (See also **A-stage, C-stage**.)

■ bubble flow

characterised by the liquid phase continuous with the gas phase, and the gas phase existing as bubbles randomly distributed.

■ bubble tight

a valve seat which closes tight enough to prevent the leakage of visible gas bubbles.

■ buckle

1) bulging of a large flat face of a casting; in investment casting, caused by dip coat peeling from the pattern, 2) an indentation in a casting, resulting from expansion of the sand, may be termed the start of an expansion defect.

■ buckling

failure mode usually characterised by unstable lateral deflection rather than breaking under compressive action.

■ buckstay

a structural member placed against a furnace or boiler wall to restrain the motion of the wall.

■ builtup plate

a pattern plate of suitable material, with the cope pattern mounted on or attached to one side; the drag pattern may be attached to the other side or to a separate mounting.

■ bulk fluid temperature

the average temperature of the process fluid at any tube cross-section.

■ **bulk density**

the ratio of the weight of a material to its over-all volume (including any inherent porosity).

■ **bumper**

a machine for ramming sand in a flask by repeated jarring or jolting.

■ **bundle**

general term for a collection of essentially parallel filaments.

■ **bundle assembly**

the name of the tubing assembly in removable bundle heat exchangers. It usually consists of tubes, tubesheets, baffles, spacers, and tierods. See Core Assembly.

■ **bunker C oil**

residual fuel oil of high viscosity commonly used in marine and stationary steam power plants.

■ **buring in**

see **Penetration, Metal.**

■ **burn**

1) process of cutting metal by a stream of fuel and oxygen, 2) to permanently damage a metal or alloy by heating to cause either incipient melting or intergranular oxidation.

■ **burned sand**

sand in which the binder or bond has been removed or impaired by contact with molten metal.

■ **burned-on-sand**

a misnomer usually indicating metal penetration into sand resulting in a mixture of sand and metal adhering to the surface of a casting.

■ **burner**

a device for the introduction of fuel and air into a furnace at the desired velocities, turbulence and concentration.

■ **burner windbox**

a plenum chamber around a burner that maintains an air pressure sufficient for proper distribution and discharge of secondary air.

■ **burner windbox pressure**

the air pressure maintained in the windbox or plenum chamber measured above atmospheric pressure.

■ **burnishing**

developing a smooth finish on a metal by tumbling or rubbing with a polished hand tool.

■ **burnthrough**

in shell moulding, resin burned out too soon.

■ **butt off**

operation performed at times to supplement ramming by jolting, either hand or air rammer.

■ **butt weld ends**

lips formed on the ends of the valve to butt against the connecting pipes. The lips on both valve and pipe are machined to form a groove to accommodate a backup ring for welding.

■ **butterfly valve**

a valve in which a disc operates at right angles to the flow. The disc may close against a metal or resilient seal.

■ **butt-welded ends**

connection element between valve body and pipeline with the purpose of body protection and adaptation to pipeline material, also for adaptation of nominal diameter.

■ **by-pass**

a passage for a fluid, permitting a portion of the fluid to flow around its normal pass flow channel.

■ **byte**

a single computer word. Depending on the hardware used, a byte may be 8, 16, 32, etc., bits.

■ **C**

carbon element, the principal combustible constituent of all fuels.

■ **C**

degrees Centigrade or Celsius.

■ **croning process**

see Shell moulding.

■ **cable cylinder**

a piston within a cylindrical housing that has a flexible cable joined to both ends. As the piston moves, it causes the cable to move over wheels at each end of the cylinder.

■ **CaCO3**

calcium Carbonate.

■ **CAD**

computer-Aided Design.

■ **CAM**

computer-aided manufacturing.

■ **CAE**

computer Aided Engineering.

■ **calcium silicide**

an alloy of Calcium, silicon, and iron containing 28-35% Ca, 60-65% Si, and 6% Fe, max., used as a deoxidiser and degasser for steel and cast-iron; sometimes called calcium silicide.

■ **calcium silicon**

an alloy of calcium, silicon, and iron containing 28-35% Ca, 60-65% Si, and 6% Fe, max., used as a deoxidiser and degasser for steel and cast-iron; sometimes called calcium silicide.

■ **calcium wired injection**

wire feeding of steel clad calcium wire into molten bath to provide favourable kinetics for inclusion modification.

■ **calorie**

the mean calorie is 1/100 of the heat required to raise the temperature of 1 gram of water from Zero C to 100 °C at a constant atmospheric pressure. It is about equal to the quantity of heat required to raise one gram of water 1 °C. Another definition is: A calorie is 3600/860 joules.

■ **calorimeter**

apparatus for determining the calorific value of a fuel.

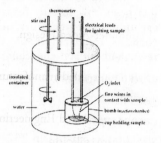

■ **cam**

a rotating part which, due to its eccentric centre line, causes an in-and-out motion in any part pushing against it.

■ **cam follower**

a special lever with a wheel at its end designed to push against a cam with little friction.

■ **camber**

deviation from edge straightness usually referring to the greatest deviation of side edge from a straight line.

■ **capacitor**

an electric device used to store electricity temporarily.

■ **capacity factor**

the ratio of the average load carried to the maximum design capacity.

■ **capscrew**

the threaded bolt used to hold the bonnet onto the core of BCF type heat exchangers. ITT Standard

uses hex head capscrews but many different head types are available. Capscrews always have a head on one end with threads at the other.

■ **carbide**

a compound of carbon with one or more metallic elements.

■ **carbon**

element occurring as diamond and as graphite. Carbon reduces many metals from their oxides when heated with the latter, and small amounts of it greatly affect the properties of iron. Though classed as a non-metallic, metallurgically, like boron, it is treated as a metal.

■ **carbon boil**

see Boil.

■ **carbon dioxide process**

also known as Silicate Process, Schmidt Philip Process. A process for hardening moulds or cores in which carbon dioxide gas is blown through dry clay-free silica sand to precipitate silica in the form of a gel from the sodium silicate binder.

■ **carbon fibre**

reinforcing fibre produced by the

pyrolysis of an organic precursor fibre, such as PAN, rayon or pitch, in an inert environment at temperatures above 1,800°F. The term carbon is often used interchangeably with the term graphite, but the fibres differ. Carbon fibres are typically carbonised at about 2,400°F and contain 93 percent to 95 percent carbon. Carbon fibres can be converted to graphite fibres by graphitisation at 3,450°F to 4,500°F, after which they contain more than 99 percent elemental carbon. Carbon fibres are known for their light weight, high strength and high stiffness.

■ **carbon sand**

a moulding aggregate consisting principally of carbon (graphite) granules.

■ **carbon, combined**

the carbon in iron or steel which is combined with other elements and therefore is not in the free state as graphite or as temper carbon.

■ **carbon/carbon**

composite of carbon fibre in a carbon matrix.

■ **carbonitriding (nicarbing)**

a process in which a ferrous alloy is case hardened by first being heated in a gaseous atmosphere of such composition that the alloy absorbs carbon and nitrogen simultaneously, and then being cooled at a rate that will produce desired properties.

■ **carburising**

a form of case hardening that produces a carbon gradient inward from the surface, enabling the surface layer to be hardened by either quenching directly from the carbonising temperature or by cooling to room temperature, then reaustenitising and quenching.

■ **card (computer)**

a printed circuit board.

■ **carnot cycle**

was first proposed in 1824 by French engineer Sadi Carnot, is composed of four reversible processes-two isothermal and two adiabatic, and can be executed either in a closed or a steady-flow system.

■ **carnot efficiency**

is the highest efficiency a heat engine operating between the two thermal energy reservoirs at temperatures T_L and T_H can have, $\varsigma_{th,rev} = 1 - T_L / T_H$.

■ **carnot heat pump**

is a heat pump that operates on the reversed Carnot cycle. When operating between the two thermal energy reservoirs at temperatures T_L and T_H the Carnot heat pump can have a coefficient of performance of $COP_{HP,rev} = 1 / (1 - T_L / T_H) = T_H / (T_H - T_L)$.

■ **carnot principles**

are two conclusions that pertain to the thermal efficiency of reversible and irreversible (i.e., actual) heat engines and are expressed as follows:

The efficiency of an irreversible heat engine is always less than the efficiency of a reversible one operating between the same two reservoirs.

The efficiencies of all reversible heat engines operating between the same two reservoirs are the same.

■ **carnot refrigerator**

is a refrigerator that operates on the reversed Carnot cycle. When operating between the two thermal energy reservoirs at temperatures T_L and T_H the Carnot refrigerator can have a coefficient of performance of $COP_{R,rev} = 1/(T_H/T_L - 1) = T_L/(T_H - T_1)$.

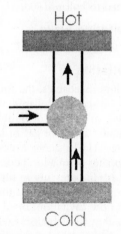

■ **carpel tunnel syndrome**

pressure on the median nerve at the point at which it passes through the carpel tunnel of the wrist. Causes soreness and tenderness of the muscles of the thumb.

■ **carrier fluid**

in impingement or slurry erosion,

fluid medium that transports impinging solid or liquid particles and that gives the particles their momentum relative to the solid surface on which they are impinging.

■ **carryover**

the chemical solids and liquid entrained with the steam from a boiler.

■ **cartesian coordinates**

a means for giving the location of a point in space by measuring its distance from a reference point along strait lines. The lines are at right angles to each other and all meet at the reference point. Named after its creator, Rene Descartes.

■ **cascade refrigeration cycles**

perform the refrigeration process in stages, that is, to have two or more refrigeration cycles that operate in series.

■ **case**

the surface layer of an iron-base alloy which has been suitably altered in composition and can be made substantially harder than the interior or core by heat treatment.

■ **case hardening**

a process of hardening a ferrous alloy so that the surface layer or case is made substantially harder than the interior or core. Typically case hardening process are carburising, carbonitriding, and nitriding.

■ **casing**

a covering of sheets of metal or

other material such as fire resistant composition board used to enclose all or a portion of a steam generating unit.

■ **casting drawing**

an engineering drawing which depicts the shape and size of a part to be cast.

■ **casting layout**

a check of dimensions against applicable drawings and specifications.

■ **cast-weld**

welding one casting to another to form a complete unit.

■ **catalyst**

substance that promotes or controls curing of a compound without being consumed in the reaction. (See also **hardener.**)

■ **catastrophic period**

in cavitation or liquid impingement erosion, a stage during which the erosion rate increases so drastically that continued exposure threatens or causes gross disintegration of the exposed surface. This stage is not inevitable; it is observed most commonly with some brittle materials. When it does occur, it may begin during any stage of the more common erosion rate-time pattern.

■ **catastrophic wear**

rapidly occurring or accelerating surface damage, deterioration, or change of shape caused by wear to such a degree that the service life of a part is appreciably shortened or its function is destroyed.

■ **caul plate**

plate or sheet the same size and shape as the composite lay-up with which it will be used. The caul plate is placed in immediate contact with the lay-up during curing to transmit normal pressure and provide a smooth surface on the finished part.

■ **cavitating disc device (or apparatus)**

a flow cavitation test device in which cavitating wakes are produced by holes in, or protuberances on, a disk rotating within a liquid-filled chamber. Erosion test specimens are attached flush with the surface of the disk, at the location where the bubbles are presumed to collapse.

■ **cavitating wake**

see **flow cavitation**.

■ **cavitation**

in fluid mechanics, the formation and subsequent collapse, within a liquid, of cavities or bubbles that contain vapour or gas or both. Notes: (1) In general, cavitation originates from a local decrease in hydrostatic pressure in the liquid, produced by motion of the liquid (see flow cavitation) or of a solid boundary (see vibratory cavitation). It is distinguished in this way from boiling which originates from an

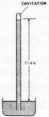

increase in liquid temperature (2) The term cavitation, by itself, should not be used to denote the damage or erosion of a solid surface that can be caused by it; this effect of cavitation is termed cavitation damage or cavitation erosion. To erode a solid surface, bubbles or cavities must collapse on or near that surface.

■ cavitation cloud

a collection of a large number of cavitation bubbles. The bubbles in a cloud are small, typically less than 1 mm (0.04 in.) in cross section. A surface that is being eroded by cavitation is usually obscured by a cavitation cloud.

■ cavitation damage

see **damage**.

■ cavitation erosion

progressive loss of original material from a solid surface due to continued exposure to cavitation.

■ cavitation erosion number

a dimensionless number that measures the tendency for cavitation to occur in a flowing stream of liquid, and that is computed from the equation:
$$s = (P_o - P_v)/(r V_o^2/2),$$
where P_v is the vapour pressure, P_o is the static pressure in the stream in an undisturbed state is the undisturbed stream velocity, and r is the liquid density.

■ cavitation erosion test

a procedure whereby the surface of a solid is subjected to cavitation attack under specified, or measurable, or at least repeatable conditions.

Such tests can be divided into two major classes depending on whether flow cavitation or vibratory cavitation is generated.

■ cavitation tunnel

a flow cavitation test facility in which liquid is pumped through a pipe or tunnel, and cavitation is induced in a test section by conducting the flow through a constriction, or around an obstacle, or a combination of these.

■ cavity

the interior opening in the mould where the part is formed.

■ celsius scale

(formerly called the *centigrade scale*; in 1948 it was renamed after the Swedish astronomer A. Celsius, 1701-1744, who devised it) is the temperature scale used in the SI system. On the Celsius scale, the ice and steam points are assigned the values of 0 and 100 °C, respectively.

■ cementite

a compound of iron and carbon commonly known as iron carbide and having the approximate chemical structure, Fe_3C. Cementite is characterised by an orthorhombic crystal structure.

■ centre of gravity (CG)

the *centre of gravity* or centre of mass of a extended body is the point in space about which the entire body balances in a uniform gravitational field. For translational dynamics, the body's entire mass can be considered as if concentrated at this point.

Every Body block has an automatic, minimum Body coordinate system (CS) with its origin at the CG - the CG CS. This origin point and the Body CS coordinate axes remain fixed rigidly in the body during the simulation.

■ central station

a power plant or steam heating plant that generates power or steam.

■ centrifugal casting

casting made in moulds which are rotating so as to produce a centrifugal force in the molten metal.

■ centrifugal fan

consists of a fan rotor or wheel within a housing that discharges air at a right angle to the axis of the wheel.

■ centrifugal pump

a pump that consists of an impeller and casing; as the impeller is put into rotation, it releases the liquid from its inner space into the casing, simultaneously increasing the energy content of the liquid.

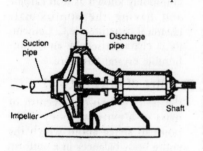

■ ceramic-matrix composites (cmc)

materials consisting of a ceramic

or carbon fibre surrounded by a ceramic matrix, primarily silicon carbide.

■ ceroxide

see **Inclusions**.

■ CG

see **centre of gravity (CG)**.

CENTER OF GRAVITY

TOTAL WEIGHT

■ chain drive

any device that transmits power by use of a chain and sprocket.

■ channel assembly

see Bonnet Assembly and Waterbox. Performs same function as bonnet assembly. However, a removable cover permits access to the ends of the tubes. Also the name of a structural construction product which is shaped like the letter 'C'.

■ chaplet

metal support that holds a core in place within a mould; molten metal solidifies around the chaplet and fuses it into the finished casting.

■ charpy impact test

a pendulum-type single-blow impact test in which the specimen, usually notched, is supported at both ends as a simple beam and broken by a falling pendulum. The energy absorbed in fracture, as impact strength or notch toughness.

■ **check valve**

a valve that allows fluid flow in one direction.

■ **cheek**

the intermediate section of a flask that is used between the cope and the drag when moulding a shape requires more than one parting plane.

■ **chemical analysis**

determination of the principal chemical constituents.

■ **chemical energy**

is the internal energy associated with the atomic bonds in a molecule.

■ **chemical equilibrium**

is established in a system when its chemical composition does not change with time.

■ **chemical equilibrium reactions**

are chemical reactions in which the reactants are depleted at exactly the same rate as they are replen-

ished from the products by the reverse reaction. At equilibrium the reaction proceeds in both directions at the same rate.

■ **chemical feed pipe**

a pipe inside a boiler drum through which chemicals for treating the boiler water are introduced.

■ **chemical potential**

is the change in the Gibbs function of the mixture in a specified phase when a unit amount of a given component of the mixture in the same phase is added as pressure and temperature and the amounts of all other components are held constant. The chemical potential of a component of an ideal gas mixture depends on the mole fraction of the components as well as the mixture temperature and pressure, and is independent of the identity of the other constituent gases.

■ **chemical vapour deposition (CVD)**

process in which the reinforcement material is deposited from the vapour phase onto a continuous core such as boron or tungsten.

■ **chemically correct amount of air**

is the stoichiometric or theoretical air, or 100 percent theoretical air.

■ **chicken wire cracks**
see **Craze Cracking**.

■ **chill (external)**

metal, graphite or carbon blocks

that are incorporated into the mould or core to locally increase the rate of heat removal during solidification and reduce shrinkage defects.

■ **chill (internal)**

a metallic device / insert in moulds or cores at the surface of a casting or within the mould to increase the rate of heat removal, include directional solidification and reduce shrinkage defects. The internal chill may then become a part of the casting.

■ **chimney**

a brick, metal or concrete stack.

■ **chip**

a single electronic part, usually to be place on a circuit board.

■ **choked flow**

flow under conditions of critical pressure and temperature. The flow rate at this point cannot be increased by lowering the outlet pressure.

■ **chromel**

a 90Ni - 10Cr alloy used in thermocouples.

■ **chromite**

$feCr_2O_4$. Specialty sand used in moulding, has a similar effect to chills.

■ **chuck**

a set of claming jaws.

■ **circulation**

the movement of water and steam within a steam generating unit.

■ **circulation ratio**

the ratio of water entering a circuit to the steam generated by that passes that circuit in a unit of time.

■ **circulator**

a pipe or tube to pass steam or water between upper boiler drums usually located where the heat absorption is low. Also used to apply to tubes connecting headers of horizontal water tube boilers with drums.

■ **circumferential winding**

process of winding fibre perpendicular to the axis during filament winding.

■ **Clapeyron equation**

after the French engineer and physicist E. Clapeyron (1799-1864), relates the enthalpy change associated with a phase change (such as the enthalpy of vapourisation h_{fg}) from knowledge of P, v, and T data alone.

■ **Clapeyron-Clausius equation**

is used to determine the variation of saturation pressure with temperature.

■ **CLAS**

a casting process in which metal fills the mould through the drag by application of a vacuum.

■ **classical thermodynamics**

is the macroscopic approach to the study of thermodynamics that does not require knowledge of the behaviour of individual particles.

Clausius inequality

first stated by the German physicist R. J. E. Clausius (1822-1888), is expressed as the cyclic integral of Q/T is always less than or equal to zero. This inequality is valid for all cycles, reversible or irreversible.

Clausius statement of the second law

is expressed as follows: It is impossible to construct a device that operates in a cycle and produces no effect other than the transfer of heat from a lower-temperature body to a higher-temperature body.

cleaning

the removal of gates, runners and risers from the rough casting. This term also involves any hand finishing such as grinding or blasting.

cleanout door

a door placed so that accumulated refuse may be removed room a boiler setting.

clearance volume

is the minimum volume formed in the cylinder when the piston is at top dead centre.

closed feedwater heater

is a feedwater heater in which heat is transferred from the extracted steam to the feedwater without any mixing taking place. The two streams are typically not at the same pressures, since they do not mix. In an ideal closed feedwater heater, the feedwater is heated to the exit temperature of the extracted steam, which ideally leaves the heater as a saturated liquid at the extraction pressure. In actual power plants, the feedwater leaves the heater below the exit temperature of the extracted steam because a temperature difference of at least a few degrees is required for any effective heat transfer to take place.

closed loop control

robot control which uses a feedback loop to measure then compare actual system performance with desired performance, and then makes adjustments accordingly.

closed loop system

you can disconnect a closed loop system into two separate systems only by cutting more than one joint. The number of closed loops is equal to the minimum number, minus one, of cuttings needed to disconnect the system into two systems.

closed system

(also known as a control mass) consists of a fixed amount of mass, and no mass can cross its boundary. But energy, in the form of heat or work, can cross the boundary.

CMC

Ceramic-matrix composite.

CMF

Cast Metals Federation.

CMM

Coordinate Measuring Machine.

CNC

Computer Numerical Controlled

Machine Tools.

■ CO
Carbon monoxide.

■ CO_2
Carbon dioxide.

■ coalescence
1) the growth of particles of a dispersed phase by solution and reprecipitation, 2) the growth of grains by absorption of adjacent undistorted grains.

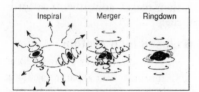

■ cobalt
blue-white metal, melting at 2715°F (1492°C), used in very hard alloy such as stellite, and a binder in carbide cutting tools.

■ cobalt-60
a radioactive isotope used in medical and industrial radiography.

■ cocoon process
a method of protecting metal parts by spraying on a cover of plastic filaments.

■ cocured
cured and simultaneously bonded to another prepared surface.

■ code
in EDP, a system of symbols and their use in representing rules for handling the flow or processing of information.

■ code holes
the information holes in perforated tape, as opposed to feed or sprocket holes.

■ coefficient of expansion
unit increase in size resulting from a unit increase in temperature; measured in inches per inch per degree Fahrenheit (in/in/1/2°F) or in millimeter per millimeter per degree Celsius (mm/mm/1/2°C).

■ coefficient of friction μ or f
in tribology, the dimension-less ratio of the friction force (F_f) between two bodies to the normal force (F_n) pressing these bodies together.

■ coefficient of performance
(COP) is the measure of performance of refrigerators and heat pumps. It is expressed in terms of the desired result for each device (heat absorbed from the refrigerated space for the refrigerator or heat added to the hot space by the heat pump) divided by the input, the energy expended to accomplish the energy transfer (usually work input).

■ coefficient of thermal expansion
a material's fractional change in length for a given unit change of temperature.

■ coercive force
the magnetising force that must be applied in the direction opposite to that of the previous magnetizing force in order to remove re-

sidual magnetism; thus, an indicator of the strength of magnetically hard materials.

■ **cogeneration**

is the production of more than one useful form of energy (such as process heat and electric power) from the same energy source.

■ **cohesion**

the force by which like particles are held together. It varies with different metals and depends upon molecular arrangement due to heat treatment.

■ **coil**

a series of tubes forming a continuous path, through which a fluid passes and heated. The heater coil consists of one or more of such tube paths in parallel.

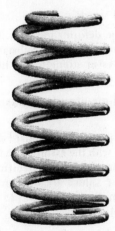

■ **coin tap**

tapping a laminate with a coin in different spots to detect a change in sound, indicating the presence of a defect that may require re-

pair.

■ **coining**

1) a process of straightening and sizing casting by die pressing, 2) a process for shaping metal.

■ **coke**

a porous, bray infusible product resulting from the dry distillation of bituminous coal, petroleum or coal tar pitch, which drives off most of the volatile matter. Used as a fuel in cupola melting.

■ **coke bed**

first layer of coke placed in the cupola. Also the coke as the foundation in constructing a large mould in a flask or pit.

■ **coke breeze**

fines from coke screening, used in blacking mixes after grinding; also briquetted for cupola use.

■ **coke furnace**

type of pot or crucible furnace using coke as the fuel.

■ **coke porosity**

the percentage volume of cell space in coke.

■ **coke, beehive**

coke produced from a bituminous coal by the beehive process where heat for the coking process comes from a partial combustion of the coke. Generally characterised by an elongate stringy structure.

■ **coke, by-product**

coke produced from bituminous coal in airtight code ovens where heat for coking process is externally applied. Generally more uniform in size than beehive coke, and usually ball or cube shape.

■ **coke, petroleum**

residue left from the distillation of petroleum crude, used as a carbon raiser.

■ **cold chamber machine**

a diecasting machine where the metal chamber and plunger are not immersed in hot metal.

■ **cold chamber, club sandwich, two-faced, three-piece die**

a diecasting die in which two different pieces are cast in two widely separated cavities.

■ **cold cracking**

cracks in cold or nearly cold metal due to excessive internal stress caused by contraction. Often brought about when the mould is to hard or casting is of unsuitable design.

■ **cold lap**

wrinkled markings on the surface of an ingot or casting from incipient freezing of the surface.

■ **cold setting binders**

term used to describe any binder that will harden the core sufficiently at room temperature so core can be removed from its box without distortion; commonly used in reference to oil-oxygen type binders.

■ **cold setting process**

an of several systems for bonding mould or core aggregates by means of organic binders, relying upon the use of catalysts rather than heat for Polymerisation (setting).

■ **cold short**

a characteristic of metals that are brittle at ordinary or low temperatures.

■ **cold shot**

small globule of metal embedded in but not entirely fused with the casting.

■ **cold shut**

casting defect caused by imperfect fusing or discontinuity of molten metal coming together from opposite directions in a mould, or due to folding of the surface. It may have the appearance of a crack or seam with smooth, rounded edges. Also see Cold Lap.

■ **cold work**

plastic deformation of a metal at room temperature. Substantial increases in strength and hardness may occur.

■ **cold-air-standard assumption**

combines the air-standard assumptions with the assumption that the air has constant specific heats whose values are determined at room temperature (25°C, or 77°F).

■ **cold-box process**

any core binder process that uses a gas or vapourised catalyst to cure a coated sand while it is in contact with the core box at room temperature.

■ collapsibity

the requirement that a sand mixture break down under the pressure and temperatures developed
during casting, in order to avoid
hot tears or facilitate the separation of the sand and the casting.

■ collapsible sprue

a sprue pattern of flexible material,
or of spring-tube design, used in
squeeze-moulding of plated patterns,
and incorporating a pouring cup.

■ collate

1) to merge items from two or
more similarly sequenced files into
one sequenced file, 2) to compare
one thing critically with another of
the same kind.

■ collection efficiency

in impingement erosion and par-
ticulate flows, the cross-sectional
area of undisturbed fluid containing particles that will all ultimately
impinge on a given solid surface,
divided by the projected area of
the solid surface, where these two
areas are perpendicular to the direction of relative motion between the solid surface and the
particles in the undisturbed fluid.
Note:(1) By "undisturbed fluid" is
meant fluid that is sufficiently
ahead of the solid surface to be
undisturbed by the flow around the
solid surface. For example, the
particles could be carried in a
stream of fluid moving toward a
solid surface that is stationary, or
the solid surface could be moving
through a suspension of particles.
Not all of the particles that move
in the direction of the solid sur-

face or lie in its path will impinge
on it, since some will be carried
away in the fluid as it flows
around the surface.
(2) A variety of terms having the
same meaning can be found in the
literature. These include "collision
efficiency," "capture efficiency,"
"catchment efficiency," "impaction
ratio," and others. The term "collection efficiency," being perhaps
the most widely used, is preferred.

■ collector

a device used for removing gas
borne solids from flue gas.

■ collet

a series of projections held in a
collar that may be tightened around
a separate shaft.

■ collimator

a device for confining the elements
of a beam of radiation within an
assigned solid angle.

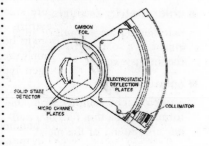

■ **collocation**

two points in space are collocated if they are coincident, within assembly tolerances.

■ **colloid**

a finely divided organic substance which tends to inhibit the formation of dense scale and results in the deposition of sludge, or causes it to remain in suspension, so that it may be blown from the boiler.

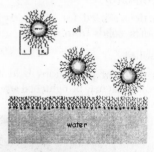

■ **colloidal clay**

finely divided clay of montmorillonite, kaolinite, or illite class; prepared for foundry purposes as in sand bonding.

■ **colloids, colloidal material**

finely divided material less than 0.5 micron (0.00002 in.) in size, such as albumin, glue, starch, gelatin, and bentonite.

■ **colorimetric analysis**

determining the amount of an element in a solution by measuring the intrinsic colour.

■ **colour etching**

a micro-etch resulting from the formation of a thin film of a definite compound of the metal.

■ **columnar structure**

a coarse structure of parallel columns of grains, which is caused by highly directional solidification.

■ **combination die (multiple-cavity die)**

in die casting, a die with two or more different cavities for different castings.

■ **combined carbon**

carbon in iron and steel which is combined chemically with other elements; not in the free state as graphitic or temper carbon.

■ **combined gas-vapour cycle**

is the gas-turbine (Brayton) cycle topping a steam-turbine (Rankine) cycle, which has a higher thermal efficiency than either of the cycles executed individually.

■ **combined water**

that water in mineral matter which is chemically combined and driven off only at temperatures above 231°F (111°C).

■ **combustible loss**

the loss representing the unliberated thermal energy occasioned by failure to oxidise completely some of the combustible matter in the fuel.

■ **combustibles**

the heat producing constituents of a fuel.

■ **combustion**

the rapid chemical combination of oxygen with the combustible elements of a fuel resulting in the release of heat.

■ combustion air

is dry air which can be approximated as 21 percent oxygen and 79 percent nitrogen by mole numbers. Therefore, each mole of oxygen entering a combustion chamber will be accompanied by $0.79/0.21 = 3.76$ mol of nitrogen. To supply one mole of oxygen to a combustion process, 4.76 mol of combustion air are required.

■ combustion chamber

see **furnace**

■ combustion efficiency

combustion equipment is defined as the amount of heat released during combustion divided by the heating value of the fuel. A combustion efficiency of 100 percent indicates that the fuel is burned completely and the stack gases leave the combustion chamber at room temperature, and thus the amount of heat released during a combustion process is equal to the heating value of the fuel.

■ combustion efficiency

the amount of heat usefully available divided by the maximum amount which can be liberated by combustion; usually expressed in percentage.

■ comfort zone (average)

the range of effective temperature over which the majority (50% or more) of adults feel comfortable.

■ commingled yarn

hybrid yarn made with two types of materials intermingled in a single yarn (for example, thermo- plastic filaments intermingled with carbon filaments to form a single yarn).

■ commonly used conversions

kPa x 0.145 = psi.
MPa x 145 = psi.
°C x 1.8 + 32 = °F.
Liters/min x 0.2642 = Gal/min.
Inches x 25.4 = mm.
Flow rate = ((number of cavities) x (volume per cavity))/(injection time).

■ comodising

a rust-proofing process for steel.

■ complete combustion

is a combustion process in which all the carbon in the fuel burns to CO_2, all the hydrogen burns to H_2O, and all the sulphur (if any) burns to SO_2. That is, all the combustible components of a fuel are burned to completion during a complete combustion process.

■ component pressure

is the pressure a component in a gas mixture would have if it existed alone at the volume and temperature of the mixture.

■ component volume

is the volume a component in a gas mixture would occupy if it existed alone at the temperature and pressure of the mixture.

■ composite

three-dimensional combination of at least two materials differing in form or composition, with a distinct interface separating the components. Composite materials are usually manmade and created to obtain properties that cannot be achieved by any of the components acting alone.

■ **composite construction**

welding a steel casting to a rolled or forged steel object or to another casting.

■ **composite joint**

a joint compounded from more than one joint primitive and thus representing more than one degree of freedom. The joint primitives constituting a composite joint are the *primitives* of that joint. A spherical primitive represents three rotational degrees of freedom, but is treated as a primitive.

■ **compressed liquid**

has a pressure greater than the saturation pressure corresponding to the temperature.

■ **compressed liquid region**

is all compressed liquid states located in the region to the left of the saturated liquid line and below the critical temperature line. In the absence of compressed liquid data, a general approximation is to treat compressed liquid as saturated liquid at the given temperature.

■ **compressibility factor**

z is a correction factor to account for deviation from ideal-gas behaviour at a given temperature and pressure. $Z = Pv/RT$.

■ **compression moulding**

technique for moulding thermoset plastics in which a part is shaped by placing the fibre and resin into an open mould cavity, closing the mould, and applying heat and pressure until the material has cured or achieved its final form.

■ **compression ratio**

r of an engine is the ratio of the maximum volume formed in the cylinder to the minimum (clearance) volume. Notice that the compression ratio is a *volume ratio* and should not be confused with the pressure ratio.

■ **compression test**

imposing a dead load on a small cylindrical test piece to determine compressive strength, expressed in pounds per sq. in.

■ **compression-ignition**

(CI) engines are reciprocating engines in which the combustion of the air-fuel mixture is self-ignited as a result of compressing the mixture above its self-ignition temperature.

■ **compressive strength**

resistance to a crushing or buckling force, the maximum compressive load a specimen sustains divided by its original cross-sectional area.

■ **compressor**

a pump which draws in air or other gases, compresses it and discharges it at a higher pressure.

■ **computer**

an electronic machine that processes information. Nowadays found in everything from children's toys and wristwatches, to automobiles and satellites..

■ **computer board**

a printed circuit board used in a computer.

■ **computer numerical control (CNC)**

the use of the dedicated computer within a numerical control unit that provides data input for the machine.

■ **computer-aided design (CAD)**

the use of a computer to assist in the design of a product or manufacturing system.

■ **computer-aided manufacturing (CAM)**

the use of a computer to assist in the manufacturing process.

■ **compressive strength (yield)**

the maximum stress in compression that can be withstood without plastic deformation or failure.

■ **contact cement**

patternmaking bonding technique, in which liquid bonding agent is painted on both surfaces to be joined and allowed to dry. These dry surfaces placed in contact adhere firmly.

■ **concentration**

1. the weight of solids contained in a unit weight of boiler or feed water.

2. The number of times that the dissolved solids have increased from the original amount in the feedwater to that in the boiler water due to evaporation in generating steam.

■ **condensate**

condensed water resulting from the removal of latent heat from steam.

■ **condensation**

polymerisation reaction in which simple by-products (for example, water) are released.

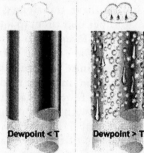

Dewpoint < T   Dewpoint > T

■ **condenser**

is a heat exchanger in which a vapour, such as steam, condenses to the saturated liquid state as the result of heat transfer from the vapour to a cooling medium such as a lake, a river, or the atmosphere.

■ **condensing rings**

a special form of chill used for cast iron to produce a dense but graphite structure.

■ **conduction**

is the transfer of energy from the

more energetic particles of a substance to the adjacent less energetic ones as a result of interaction between particles.

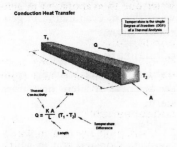

Conduction Heat Transfer

Temperature is the single Degree-of-freedom (DOF) of a Thermal Analysis

$$Q = \frac{KA}{L}(T_1 - T_2)$$

Thermal Conductivity, Area, Temperature Difference, Length

■ conductivity

1) a material property relating heat flux (heat transferred per unit area per unit time) to a temperature difference. In American units, it is typically defined as the amount of heat (Btu) transmitted in one hour through one square foot of material 1 inch thick, with a temperature difference of 1°F between the two surfaces of the material. 2) The property of a water sample to transmit electric current under a set of standard conditions. Usually expressed as microhms conductance.

■ connection line

you connect each block to another by using *connection lines*. These lines function only with Mechanics blocks. They do not carry signals, unlike normal Linklines, and cannot be branched. You cannot link connection lines directly to Linklines.

Connection lines appear red and dashed if they are not anchored at both ends to a connector port

O. Once you so anchor them, the lines become black and solid.

■ connor gate (runner) (lip feeder)

a runner in which the feed block overlaps the casting by 1/16 in. (1.6 mm).

■ conservation of energy principle

or energy balance based on the first law of thermodynamics may be expressed as follows: Energy can be neither created nor destroyed; it can only change forms. The net change (increase or decrease) in the total energy of the system during a process is equal to the difference between the total energy entering and the total energy leaving the system during that process. The energy balance can be written explicitly as $E_{in} - E_{out} = (Q_{in} - Q_{out}) + (W_{in} - W_{out}) + (E_{mass,\ in} - E_{mass,\ out}) = \ddot{A}E_{system}$.

■ conservation of mass principle

is expressed as net mass transfer to or from a system during a process equal to the net change (increase or decrease) in the total mass of the system during that process.

■ conservation of mass principle (or the mass balance)

is the principle used to balance chemical reaction equations. It can be stated as follows: The total mass of each element is conserved during a chemical reaction.

The total mass of each element on the right-hand side of the reaction equation (the products) must be equal to the total mass of that element on the left-hand side (the reactants) even though the elements exist in different chemical compounds in the reactants and products. Even though the mass must be conserved, the total number of moles is not conserved during a chemical reaction.

■ consolidation

processing step that compresses fibre and matrix to reduce voids and achieve a particular density.

■ constant intensity pyrometer

use of a comparison lamp filament's glow to estimate metal temperature.

■ constant pressure gradient

pressure drop per unit length. The constant pressure gradient principle says that the most efficient filling pattern is when the pressure gradient is constant along the flow path.

■ constantan

an alloy of nickel and copper use in thermocouples.

■ constituent

a micrographically distinguishable part of an alloy or mixture.

■ constrained joint

a composite joint with one or more built-in constraints relating the joint's primitives.
An example is the Screw block, which has a prismatic and a revo-lute primitive with their motions in fixed ratio. Only one of these degrees of freedom is independent.

■ constraint

a restriction among degrees of freedom imposed independently of any applied forces/torques. A constraint removes one or more independent degrees of freedom, unless that constraint is redundant and restricts degrees of freedom that otherwise could not move anyway. Constraints can also create inconsistencies with the applied forces/torques that lead to simulation errors.
Constraints are kinematic: they must involve only coordinates and/or velocities. Higher derivatives of coordinates (accelerations, etc.) are determined by the Newtonian force/torque equations and cannot be independently constrained.
Constraints can be holonomic (integrable into a form involving only coordinates) or non-holonomic (not integrable; that is, irreducibly involving velocities).
The relationship specified by a constraint can be an explicit function of time (rheonomic) or not (scleronomic).

■ consumer's risk

the risk the consumer runs of accepting lots of quality p2.

■ contact drum

a cylinder with electrical conducting strips around its exterior that, when rotated, will cause the connection of electrical contacts.

■ **contact printing (ink print)**

a method of recording details of a macroetched structure.

■ **contact sensor**

a device that detects the presence of a n object or measures the amount of force or torque applied by the object through physical contact with it.

■ **containment units**

an active entity designed to represent a family of contingency plans parameterised by resource commitments. As the control context changes, it manages reserved resources to produce and maintain a stream of information subject to real-time, livemness, and performance constraints.

■ **contamination**

1) radioactive deposition of radioactive material in any place where it is not desired, and particularly in any place where its presence may be harmful. The harm may be in vitiating the validity of an experiment or a procedure, or in actually being a source of danger to personnel, 2) presence of small percentages of deleterious elements in an alloy adversely affecting the alloy's mechanical properties and/or casting soundness.

■ **continuous tapping**

a furnace or holding ladle that is made of discharge molten metal continuously during normal operation.

■ **continuity equation**

is the conservation of mass equa-

tion as it is often referred to in fluid mechanics.

■ **continuous annealing furnace**

furnace in which castings are annealed or heat treated by passing through different zones at constant temperatures.

■ **continuous blowdown**

the uninterrupted removal of concentrated boiler water from a boiler to control total solids concentration in the remaining water.

■ **continuous desulphurisation**

a process of removing sulphur from molten ferrous alloys on a continuous basis.

■ **continuous filament**

individual, small-diameter reinforcement that is flexible and indefinite in length.

■ **continuous jet**

see **liquid jet**.

■ **continuous mixer**

used to continuously mix chemically bonded sand.

■ **continuous phase**

the phase that forms the matrix or background in which the other phases are present as isolated units.

■ **continuous roving**

large bundle of parallel filaments coated with sizing, gathered together into single or multiple strands, and wound into a cylindrical package. May be used to provide continuous reinforcement in woven roving, filament winding, pultrusion, prepregs, or high-strength moulding compounds (may also be used chopped).

■ **continuum**

is a view of mass as continuous, homogeneous matter with no holes. Matter is made up of atoms that are widely spaced in the gas phase. Yet it is very convenient to disregard the atomic nature of a substance. The continuum idealisation allows us to treat properties as point functions, and to assume the properties to vary continually in space with no jump discontinuities. This idealisation is valid as long as the size of the system we deal with is large relative to the space between the molecules. This is the case practically in all problems, except some specialised ones.

■ **controlled area**

a defined area in which the occupational exposure of personnel to radiation or to radioactive material is under the supervision of an individual in charge of radiation protection.

■ **contraction**

the volume change occurring in metals (except antimony and bismuth) and alloys on solidification and cooling to room temperature.

■ **contraction cracks**

cracks formed by restriction of the metal while contracting in the mould; may occur just after solidification (called a hot tear) or a short time after the casting has been removed from the mould.

■ **contraction rule**

see **Shrinkage, Patternmaker's.**

■ **control**

any manual or automatic device for the regulation of a machine to keep it at normal operation. If automatic, the device is motivated by variations in temperature, pressure, water level, time, light, or other influences.

■ **control architecture**

the principled organisation of embedded software components whereby perception, reasoning, and action conspire to produce functionality. This architecture not only provides structure and services, but guides design by imposing methodological constraints on how Behaviour can be achieved.

■ **control surface**

is the boundary of a control volume, and it can be real or imaginary.

■ **control valve**

a valve which regulates the flow or pressure of a medium which affects some controlled process. Control valves are usually operated by remote signals from independent devices using control mechanisms powered electrically, pneumatically, electro-hydraulically, etc.

■ **control volume, or open system**

is any arbitrary region in space through which mass and energy can pass across the boundary. Most control volumes have fixed

boundaries and thus do not involve any moving boundaries. A
control volume may also involve
heat and work interactions just as
a closed system, in addition to mass
interaction.

controlled atmosphere

any gas or mixture of gases that
prevents or retards oxidation and
decarburisation.

controlled cooling
see **Cooling, Controlled.**

controlled frictional heating

runners designed to deliver a
higher melt temperature to the
cavity. This results in lower stress
levels in the part without causing
material degradation due to long
exposure to elevated temperatures.

controller

every robot is connected to a computer, which keeps the pieces of
the arm working together. This
computer is known as the controller. The controller functions as the
'brain' of the robot. Robots today
have controllers that are run by
programs - sets of instructions
written in code. Almost all robots
of today are entirely pre-programmed by people; they can do
only what they are programmed
to do at the time, and nothing else.
In the future, controllers with artificial intelligence, or AI could allow robots to think on their own,
even program themselves. This
could make robots more self-reli-
ant and independent.

convection

the transmission of heat by the

circulation of a liquid or gas. It
may be natural, with the circulation caused by buoyancy affects
due to temperature differences, or
forced with circulation caused by
a mechanical device such as a fan
or pump.

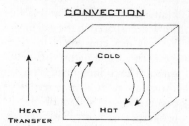

CONVECTION

convection section

the portion of a heater, consisting
of a bank of tubes or coils, which
receives heat from hot flue gases,
mainly by convection.

converging-diverging nozzles

are ducts in which the flow area
first decreases and then increases
in the direction of the flow.

converter

a furnace in which a gas, usually
air, is blown through the molten
bath or crude metal for the purpose of oxidising impurities.

convery, vibratory

a materials-handling device used
usually with shakeout operations,
to help clean sand from the castings as they are moved from one
place to another in the foundry and
as a feeding device to regulate
materials flow. Operations with
vibrational energy.

Vibratory Screens

■ convex hull

the surface of minimum area with convex (outward-bowing) curvature that passes through all the spatial points in a set. In three dimensions, this set must contain at least four non-coplanar points to make a closed surface with non-zero enclosed volume.

In Mechanics, the convex hull is an option for visualising a body. The set of points is all the Body coordinate system (CS) origins configured in that Body block. The visualisation of an entire machine is the set of the convex hulls of all its bodies.

If a Body has fewer than four non-coplanar Body CSs, its convex hull is a lower-dimensional figure: three Body CSs produce a triangle without volume; two Body CSs produce a line without area; and one Body CS (the CS at the centre of gravity) a point without length.

■ conveyor

a mechanical apparatus for carrying or transporting materials from place to place. Types include apron, belt, chain, gravity, roller, monorail, overhead, pneumatic, vibrating, etc.

■ conveyor belt

a continuously moving belt used in an automated or semiautomatic foundry to move materials from one station to another.

■ conveyor screw

rotary worm-type blade used to move materials in automated core and mould making and other continuous sand-mixing operations.

■ conveyor, pallet

a materials-handling device that holds one or more moulds and transports them from the moulding station through pouring to shakeout.

■ conveyor, pneumatic tube

an air-tube means of moving materials from on place to another, primarily orders, light metal samples, and sand and other finely divided materials, as bentonite.

■ conveyor, roller

a line of conveyance in an automated or semiautomated foundry which employs a series of steel roller for moving objects.

■ conveyor, slat

a materials-handling device built on a continuous belt of metal slats that moves granular materials and castings throughout a foundry.

■ cooler

the largest of three water coolers surrounding the cinder notch of a blast furnace.

■ cooling capacity

is the rate of heat removal from the refrigerated space by a refrigeration system.

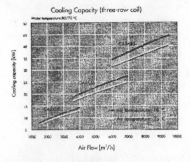

Cooling Capacity (three-row coil)
Water temperature 80/70 °C

Cooling capacity [kW]

Air Flow [m³/h]

cooling curve

a curve showing the relationship between time and temperature during the solidification and cooling of a metal sample. Since most phase changes involve evolution or absorption of heat, there may be abrupt changes in the slope of the curve.

cooling fin

see **Cracking Strip**.

cooling fins

are used for medium temperatures of over 300°C for protection of stuffing box and actuator. Furthermore with these the thickness of the pipeline insulation is considered.

cooling pond

is a large lake open to the atmosphere into which warm water containing waste heat is pumped. Heat transfer from the pond surface to the atmosphere is very slow, thus about 20 times the area of a spray pond is needed in this case to achieve the same cooling.

cooling stress

stresses developed by uneven con-traction or external constraint of metal during cooling.

cooling time

the elapsed time required for the melt to reach its softening temperature.

cooling, controlled

a process of cooling from an elevated temperature in a predetermined manner used to produce a desired microstructure to avoid hardening, cracking or internal damage.

coordinate axes

see laminate coordinate axes.

coordinate system (CS)

a *coordinate system* is defined, in a particular reference frame (RF), by a choice of *origin* and orientation of *coordinate axes*, assumed orthogonal and Cartesian (rectangular). An observer attached to that CS measures distances from that origin and directions relative to those axes.

cope

upper or topmost section of a flask, mould or pattern.

cope, false

temporary cope used only in forming the parting and therefore not a part of the finished mould.

coping out

the extension of sand of the cope downward into the drag, where it takes an impression of a pattern.

copper

for foundry applications, copper

is meant to include all alloys containing 98% or more copper. Used for conductivity castings. Melting point 1083°C (1981.4°F).

■ **copper, electrolytic**

copper produced by the electrolysis method.

■ **corbels**

narrow ledges extending from the convection section sidewalls to prevent flue gas from flowing preferentially up the side of the convection section, between the wall and the nearest tubes, thereby bypassing the tube bank.

■ **core**

in sandwich construction, the central component to which inner and outer skins are attached; also refers to a section of a complex mould that forms undercut parts.

■ **core arbor**

an iron framework embedded in a large core to stiffen it and for convenience in handling.

■ **core assembly**

the name of the shell assembly and tube assembly in fixed tubesheet heat exchangers.

■ **core barrel**

pipe-shaped device upon which a cylindrical core is formed.

■ **core binder**

any material used to hold the grains of core sand together.

■ **core blow**

a gas pocket in a casting adjacent to a core cavity caused by entrapping gases from the core.

■ **core box, combination**

core box and core dryers from the same pattern. One half is used as a half core box and a core drier.

■ **core branch**

part of a core assembly.

■ **core breaker**

a machine for crushing cores or for removing cores from castings.

■ **core cavity**

the interior form of a core box that gives shape to the core. Also, the cavity produced in a casting by use of a core.

■ **core collapsibility**

the rate of disintegration of the core at elevated temperature.

■ **core compound**

a commercial mixture used as a binder in core sand.

■ **core crab**

an iron framework embedded in a large core to stiffen it and for convenience in handling.

■ **core crush**

compression damage of the core.

■ **core density**

1) Permeability of core or 2) weight per unit volume.

■ **core depression**

gouge or indentation in the core material.

■ **core driers**

supports used to hold cares in shape while being baked; constructed from metals or sand for conventional baking, or from plastic material for use with dielectric core-baking equipment.

■ **core extruder**

a special shell-core-making machine that produces a continuous length of cores, usually of cylindrical cross-section.

■ **core filler**

material used in place of sand in the interiors of large cores - coke, cinder, sawdust, etc. usually added to aid collapsibility.

■ **core fin**

a casting defect, a depression in the casting caused by a fin on the core that was not removed before the core was set, or by paste that has oozed out from between the joints.

■ **core float**

a casting defect caused by core movement towards the cope surface of the mould, as a result of core buoyancy in liquid steel, resulting in a deviation from the intended wall thickness.

■ **core frame**

frame of skeleton construction used instead of a complete core box in forming intermediate and large cores.

■ **core grinder**

machine for grinding a taper on the end of a cylindrical core or to grind a core to a specified dimension, usually flat face.

■ **core gum**

a pitch material used as a core binder.

■ **core hardness**

the ability of a core to resist scratching or abrasion.

■ **core jig**

a device for setting core assemblies outside of the mould and placing the whole assembly in the mould.

■ **core knockout machine**

a mechanical device for removing cores from castings.

■ **core lightener**

a core material of any size and shape used to lighten pattern castings and match plates.

■ **core maker**

a core seat so shaped or arranged

that the core will register correctly in the mould; also termed locator, indicator, register, telltale.

■ **core mud**

a daubing mixture used to correct defect in cores.

■ **core orientation**

used on a honeycomb core to line up the ribbon direction, thickness of the cell depth, cell size and transverse direction.

■ **core prints**

portions of a pattern that locate and anchor the core in the proper position in the sand.

■ **core refractiveness**

the ability of a core to resist breakdown when exposed to heat.

■ **core rod**

a wire or rod of steel used to reinforce and stiffen the core.

■ **core sand**

sand for making cores to which a binding material has been added to obtain good cohesion and permeability after drying. Usually low in clays.

■ **core setting jig**

a device used to help set a core into the mould.

■ **core setting jig/gauge**

a device used to help position a core in the mould.

■ **core shift**

a variation from specified dimensions of a cored section due to a change in position of the core or

misalignment of cores in assembling.

■ **core shooter**

a device using low air pressure to fluidise the sand mix which is released quickly in such a way as to force it into a core box.

■ **core spindle**

a shaft on which a core barrel is rotated in making cylindrical cores.

■ **core splicing**

joining of two core segments by bonding them together.

■ **core sprayer**

a device for spraying a coating on cores.

■ **core stickle template (sweep)**

device of wood or metal to give shape to certain types of cores or moulds.

■ **core strainer (strainer tub)**

baked sand or refractory disc with uniform size holes through its thickness used to control the discharge of metal from pouring basins into sprues or to regulate the flow of metal in gates systems of moulds; also to prevent entrance of dross or slag into the mould cavity.

■ **core truck**

truck or carriage used for transporting cores.

■ **core vents**

1. holes made in the core for escape of gas.
2. A metal screen or slotted piece

used to form the vent passage in the core box employed in a core-blowing machine.
3. A wax product, round or oval in form, used to form the vent passage in a core.

■ **core wires or rolls**
see **Core Rod.**

■ **core-baking dielectric**
heating cores to baking temperatures by means of high-frequency dielectric equipment; particularly adapted to thermo-setting resin core binders.

■ **coreless induction furnace**
see **induction furnace.**

■ **core-mading machine**
a device to make cores.

■ **coremaker**
a craftsman skilled in the production of cores for foundry use.

■ **corer, sag**
a decrease in the height of a core, usually accompanied by an increase in width, as a result of insufficient green strength of the sand to support its own weight.

■ **coring (metallurgical)**
variable composition due to the solidification characteristics of an alloy. Typically these compositional differences occur on a micro scale, the distances between compositional extremes being controlled by the solidification structure of the alloy.

■ **coring up**
placement of cores chills, and

chaplets in mould halves before closing the mould.

■ **cornerslick (inside and outside corners)**
a moulder's tool used for repairing and slicking the sand in moulds. Used primarily on Dry sand and loam.

■ **corrective effective temperature chart**
a chart on which information can be plotted resulting in an adjustment temperature reading more indicative of human comfort.

■ **corrosion**
1. gradual chemical or electro-chemical attack on a metal by atmosphere, moisture or other agents.
2. chemical attack of furnace linings by gases, slags, ashes or other fluxes occurring in various melting practices.

■ **corrosion index**
a number expressing the maximum depth in mils to which corrosion would penetrate in one year on the basis of a linear extrapolation of the penetration occurring during the lifetime of a given test or service.

■ **corrosion wear**
wear in which chemical or electrochemical reaction with the environment is significant.

■ **corundum**
native alumna, or aluminium oxide, Al_2O_3, occurring as rhombohedral crystals and also in masses and variously coloured grains. Ap-

plied specifically to non-transparent kinds used as abrasives. It is the hardest mineral except the diamond. Corundum and its artificial counterparts are abrasives especially suited to the grinding of metals.

■ **coslettising**

producing a black, rust-resisting surface on iron and steel by boiling for some hours in water containing phosphoric acid and iron filings.

■ **cottrell process**

an electrostatic method of removing solid particles from gases.

■ **count rate meter**

a device which gives a continuous indication of the average rate of ionising events.

■ **couple**

two dissimilar conductors in electrical contact. An electromotive force in created under proper electrolytic influences or during heating.

■ **coupling**

the name of a part which is used to connect customers's piping to our heat exchangers. At ITT Standard these couplings rarely exceed 3" sizes. Couplings come in many styles. The most used style at ITT Standard being the half couplings which we use for vent and drain pipe tap connections.

■ **courses**

alternate layers of material in a pattern, or brickwork.

■ **cover**

a protective blanket laid on a melt to exclude oxidising atmosphere and in the case of magnesium to prevent its igniting. Neutral covers simply protect metal from atmosphere; reacting covers contain an agent such as a deoxidiser.

■ **cover core**

a core set in place during the ramming of a mould to cover and complete a cavity partly formed by the withdrawal of a loose part of the pattern. Also used to form part or all of the cope surface of the mould cavity. A core placed over another core to create a flat parting line.

■ **cover half**

in die casting, the stationary half of the die.

■ **cover/cover assembly**

the name of the part which is used to cover an opening on a heat exchanger. Channel covers are used in conjunction with channels to seal off the tubeside of the heat exchanger. Nozzle covers can be used to cover nozzle openings to keep heat exchanger internals clean during shipping and storage. Covers are different from end plates in the sense that they can be removed from the heat exchanger to clean the interior of the tubeside, without disturbing any piping.

■ **cowoven fabric**

reinforcement fabric woven with

two different types of fibres in individual yarns (for example, thermoplastic fibres woven side by side with carbon fibres).

■ **crab**

see **Core Crab**.

■ **crack, hot tear**

a rupture occurring in a casting at or just below the solidifying temperature by a pulling apart of the soft metal, caused by thermal contraction stresses.
See also Quench Crack.

■ **cracking strip**

a fin of metal moulded on the surface of a casting to prevent cracking.

■ **cradle assembly**

the name of the part used to support the entire heat exchanger. Cradles may be fixed or moveable. Is also used to secure the heat exchanger to the customer's mounting surface, when they are welded or strapped to the shell.

■ **crane**

a machine for lifting heavy weights; may be hand or power operated. Type include electric, gantry, jib, monorail, etc.

■ **crane, gantry**

a bridge carrying a travelling crane and supported by a pair of trestles running on parallel tracks.

■ **crane, jib**

a crane suspended from a jib.

■ **crane, mobile**

a crane supported on structure that rolls on wheels; may be moved manually or by its own power.

■ **crane, wall jib**

a jib crane mounted on a wall rather than on an overhead beam.

■ **craze crack (crazing)**

minute crack on ceramic or refractory surface caused by thermal or mechanical shock.

■ **crazing**

region of ultrafine cracks that may develop on or under a resin surface.

■ **crazing (worming)**

a defect found in pack-hardened tools, manifested in surface markings.

■ **creep**

the flow or plastic deformation of metals held for long periods of time at stresses lower than the normal yield strength. The effect is particularly important if the temperature of stressing is in the vicinity of the recrystallisation temperature of the metal.

■ **creep limit**

the maximum stress that will result in creep at a rate lower than an assigned rate.

■ **crib**

network of cast iron used to support the cope when no cope flask is used.

■ **crimp**

degree of waviness of a fibre, which determines its capacity to cohere.

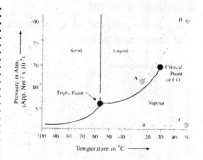

■ **cristobalite**

simplest crystallographic form of SiO_2.

■ **criterion for chemical equilibrium**

is the equation set equal to zero that involves the stoichiometric coefficients and the molar Gibbs functions of the reactants and the products in the equilibrium reaction.

■ **critical cooling rate**

the minimum rate of continuous cooling just enough to prevent undesired transformations.

■ **critical length**

minimum length of a fibre necessary for matrix shear loading to develop ultimate fibre strength.

■ **critical point**

is defined as the point at which the saturated liquid and saturated vapour states are identical.

■ **critical pressure**

the ratio of downstream to upstream pressure at which the media is just beginning to exhibit flashing or cavitation.

■ **critical properties**

are the properties of a fluid at a location where the Mach number is unity.

■ **critical ratios**

are the ratios of the stagnation to static properties when the Mach number is unity.

■ **critical shear stress**

the shear stress required to cause slip in a single crystal, in a designated slip direction on a given slip plane. Referred to as the critical resolved shear stress if the shear stress reaches a threshold level.

■ **critical strain**

a term used in stress corrosion cracking tests to indicate the maximum strain rate necessary to promote stress corrosion cracks.

■ **critical temperature**

T_{cr} is the temperature of a substance at the critical point.

critical volume

V_{cr} is the volume of a substance at the critical point.

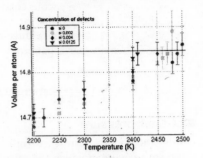

Croning process

a casting process name after its German developer Johannes Croning. It is a precision production process using a phenol formaldehyde resin binder.
See Shell moulding.

cross gate

see **runner**.

cross section

a view of the interior of an object that is represented as being cut in two, the cut surface presenting the cross section of the object.

crossbar

wood or metal bar placed in a flask to give greater anchorage to the sand than is afforded by its four walls.

cross-laminated

laminated with some of the layers oriented at one or more angles to the other layers with respect to the principal laminate axis.

Crosslinking

polymerisation reactions that branch out from the main molecular chain to form a networked pattern of chemical links.

Cross linking – alkoxy exchange

$Ti(OR)_4 + R'OH \longrightarrow (R'O)Ti(OR')_3 + R'OH \uparrow$

$Ti(OR)_4$ + Hydroxylated polymer or substrate :

crossply laminate

laminate having plies oriented only at 0° and 90°. May or may not be symmetric.

crown

furnace roof, especially when dome-shaped; highest point of an arch.

crown sheet

in a firebox boiler, the plate forming the top of the furnace.

crucible

a ceramic pot or receptacle made of materials such as graphite or silicon carbide, with relatively high thermal conductivity, bonded with clay or carbon, and used in melting metals; sometimes applied to pots made of cast iron, steel, or wrought steel. The name derives from the cross (Crux) with which ancient alchemists adorned it.

crucible furnace

a furnace fired with coke, oil, gas, or electricity in which metals are melted in a refractory crucible.

■ **crucible zone**

the zone in the cupola between the bottom and the tuyere.

■ **crude oil**

unrefined petroleum.

■ **crush**

buckling or breaking of a section of mould due to incorrect register when closing. Also, an indentation in the casting surface due to displacement of sand in the mould when the mould is closed.

■ **crush strip or bead**

an indentation in the parting line of a pattern plate which ensures that cope and drag have good contact by producing a ridge of sand which crushes against the other surface of the mould or core.

■ **cryogenic valve**

a valve used to control the flow of cryogenic liquid.

■ **cryogenics**

the science dealing with the prop-

erties of water at temperatures near absolute zero.

■ **crystal**

a physically homogeneous solid in which the atoms, ions, or molecules are arranged in a three-dimensional repetitive pattern.

■ **crystal analysis**

determination of crystal structure.

■ **crystal lattice**

the way atoms are arranged in a crystal. Spacewise, there are only 14 different lattices.

■ **crystalline**

material assuming fixed internal forms. Slow cooling areas have high crystallinity and shrinkage.

■ **crystalline fracture**

fracture of a brittle metal, showing definite crystal faces in the fractured surface.

■ **crystallisation**

the formation of crystals by the atoms assuming definite positions in the crystal lattice, e.g. when a metal solidifies.

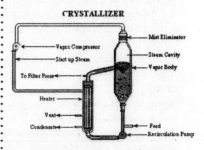

CRYSTALLIZER

■ **CS**

a coordinate system (CS).

■ CSD-1

abbreviation for the ASME standard for Controls and Safety Devices.

■ C-stage

final step in the cure of a thermoset resin, resulting in irreversible hardening and insolubility. (See also A-stage and B-stage.)

■ CTD

Cumulative Trauma Disorder. Illnesses that develop gradually over time and involve disorders of the soft tissues of the body. Caused or aggravated by repeatedly or constantly applied excessive forces, awkward postures, or highly repetitive movements of the body.

■ CTE

see coefficient of thermal expansion.

■ cumulative erosion

in cavitation and impingement erosion, the total amount of material lost from a solid surface during all exposure periods since it was first exposed to cavitation or impingement as a newly-finished surface. (More specific terms that may be used are cumulative mass loss, cumulative volume loss, or cumulative mean depth of erosion: See also cumulative erosion-time curve.)

Notes- Unless otherwise indicated by the context, it is implied that the conditions of cavitation or impingement have remained the same throughout all exposure periods with no intermediate refinishing of the surface.

■ cumulative erosion rate

the cumulative erosion at a specified point in an erosion test divided by the corresponding cumulative exposure duration: that is, the slope of a line from the origin to the specified point on the cumulative erosion-time curve. (Synonym: average erosion rate).

■ cumulative erosion-time curve

in cavitation and impingement erosion, a plot of cumulative erosion versus cumulative exposure duration, usually determined by periodic interruption of the test and weighing of the specimen. This is the primary record of an erosion test. Most other characteristics, such as the incubation period, maximum erosion rate, terminal erosion rate, and erosion rate-time curve, are derived from it.

■ cure

to change the physical properties of a material irreversibly by chemical reaction via heat and/or catalysts, with or without pressure.

■ cure temperature

temperature at which a material attains final cure.

■ curing agent

catalytic or reactive agent that brings about Polymerisation when added to a resin.

■ curing time (no bake)

that period of time needed before a sand mass reaches maximum hardness.

■ cushion

a device used to provide controlled resistance to motion.

■ cushion, cylinder

a cushion built into a cylinder to restrict the flow at the outlet and thereby arrest the motion of the piston rod.

■ cut

defect in a casting resulting from erosion of the sand by metal flowing over the mould or cored surface.

■ cutoff machine, abrasive

a device using a thin abrasive wheel rotating at high speed to cut off gates and risers from castings, or in similar operations.

■ cutoff ratio

r_c is the ratio of the cylinder volumes after and before the combustion process in the Diesel cycle.

■ cutter, gate

a scoop or other form of cutting gates in the mould.

■ cutting wheel

the plastic discs impregnated with an abrasive for cutting ceramics and metals. Used on abrasive cutoff machines.

■ CVD

see **chemical vapour deposition**.

■ cybernetics

an emerging field of study that explores the integration of the

robot hardware design overview

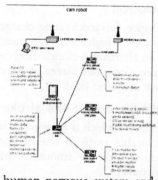

human nervous system and human-made technological devices, such as microchips, robotic components, 'nano' machines, and electronics.

■ cycle

is a process, or series of processes, that allows a system to undergo state changes and returns the system to the initial state at the end of the process. That is, for a cycle the initial and final states are identical.

■ cycle time

elapsed time between a certain point in one cycle and the same point in the next cycle.

■ cyclone (centrifugal collector)

in air pollution control, a controlled descending vortex created to spiral objectionable gases and dust to the bottom of a collector core.

cyclonic scrubber

in air pollution control, radial liquid (usually water) sprays introduced into cyclones to facilitate collection of particles.

cyclotron

a device for accelerating charged particles to high energies by means of an alternating electric field between electrodes placed in a constant magnetic field.

cylinder, adjustable stroke

a cylinder which is equipped with adjustable stops at one or both ends to limit the amount of piston travel.

cylinder, double acting

a cylinder in which the fluid can be applied to the movable element in either direction.

cylinder, double-end-rod

a cylinder which has a rod extending from each end.

cylinder, single acting

a cylinder in which the fluid can be applied to the movable element in only one direction.

d (Fordath) process

shell moulding in which the shell is made by blowing sand into a box like heated structure so that a shell of controlled thickness is created.

Dalton's law of additive pressures

the pressure of a gas mixture is equal to the sum of the pressures each gas would exert if it existed alone at the mixture temperature and volume.

damage

in cavitation or impingement, any effect on a solid body resulting from its exposure to these phenomena. This may include loss of material, surface deformation, or any other changes in microstructure, properties, or appearance.

Notes This term as here defined should normally be used with the appropriate modifier, for example, 'cavitation damage,' 'liquid impingement damage,' 'single-impact damage,' etc.

damage tolerance

measure of the ability of structures to retain load-carrying capability after exposure to sudden loads (for example, ballistic impact).

damper

a device to regulate flow of gas through a stack or duct and to control draft in a heater. A typical damper consists of a flat plate connected to a shaft, which can be rotated, similar to a butterfly valve. A damper may have more than one blade.

■ damping

diminishing the intensity of vibrations.

■ data

information stored by a computer. This information is almost always digital, or stored in the binary form of 1's and 0's.

■ datum plane

in layout and machining operations the reference plane from which dimensions are measured in the perpendicular direction.

■ datum points

in layout and machining operations the reference points on a datum plane from which dimensions are measured.

■ daubing

filling of cracks in moulds or cores by specially prepared pastes or coatings to prevent a mechanical penetration of metal into these cracks during pouring. Also, the final plastering or coating of the cupola or ladle after shrinkage has taken place during the drying period. Clay slurry or clay wash with various coating compounds are applied.

■ DAVIT

the structure on large firetube boilers from which the front and rear doors are suspended when opened.

■ dB

see **decibel**.

■ dBA

a rating system used to measure the amount the harmful effect of sound. dB equals decibels, A the specific scale (there are also B and C scales).

■ dc (direct chill) casting

a continuous method of making ingots or billets or extrusion by pouring the metal into a short mould. Some times called semi-continuous casting.

■ dead annealing

see **annealing**.

■ dead band

a specific range of values in which an input signal can be altered without causing a change in the output signal.

■ dead state

is a state a system is said to be in when it is in thermodynamic equilibrium with its environment.

■ dead steel

fully killed steel, also applied to steel which fails to respond to heat treatment.

■ deadburned

term applied to refractory materials obtained by calcimining at a temperature high enough to form a product inert to atmospheric moisture and carbon dioxide, and less apt to contract.

deadburned dolonite

dolonite burned at high temperature with additions of an agent, such as oxide of iron.

deadhead

the useless metal projecting on a casting which corresponds to the position of a riser in the mould.

deaeration

removal of air and gases from boiler feed water prior to its introduction to a boiler.

debond

deliberate separation of a bonded joint or interface, usually for repair or rework purposes. (See also **disbond**.)

debris

in tribology, particles that have become detached in a wear or erosion process.

deburring

the process of removing burrs from a part, also rounding sharp edges.

decant

1. pour from one vessel to another
2. pour off molten metal without disturbing the sludge.

decarburistion

loss of carbon from the surface of a ferrous alloy as a result of heating in a medium, usually oxygen, that react with carbon.

deceleration period

in cavitation or liquid impingement erosion, the stage following the acceleration period or the maximum rate period (if any), during which the erosion rate has an overall decreasing trend although fluctuations may be superimposed on it.

decibel (dB)

unit for measuring amounts of acoustical power; one-tenth of a bel.

decrease of exergy principle

can be expressed as the exergy of an isolated system during a process always decreases or, in the limiting case of a reversible process, remains constant. In other words, it never increases and exergy is destroyed during an actual process. For an isolated system, the decrease in exergy equals exergy destroyed.

deep etching

macroetching; etching for examination at a low (less that 10X) magnification, in a reagent that attacks the metal to a much greater extent than normal for microscopic examination. Gross features my be developed; i.e., abnormal grain size, segregation, cracks, or grain flow.

deepbed filter

a gas filter in air pollution control, consisting of a loosely packed mat of fibrous materials; not practical where high grain loading are encountered.

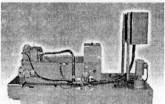

■ **defect**

a discontinuity in the product whose severity is judged unacceptable in accordance with the applicable product specification.

■ **deficiency of air**

results when the amounts of air are less than the stoichiometric amount.

■ **deformation test**

an AGS test using an instrument such as the Dietert Universal Sand-Strength Testing machine (with deformation accessory) to determine the amount in inches that the sand specimen is compressed before it ruptures.

■ **degassification**

removal of gases from samples of steam taken for purity test. Removal of CO_2 from water as in the ion exchange method of softening.

■ **degasser**

a material employed for removing gases from molten metals and alloys.

■ **degassing**

usually a chemical reaction resulting from a compound added to molten metal to remove gases from the metal. Often inert gases are used in this operation.

■ **degassing flux**

a flux for removing gas from the melt.

■ **degree of freedom (DoF)**

a single coordinate of relative motion between two bodies. Such a coordinate is free only if it can respond without constraint or imposed motion to externally applied forces or torques. For translational motion, a DoF is a linear coordinate along a single direction. For rotational motion, a DoF is an angular coordinate about a single, fixed axis. A prismatic joint primitive represents a single translational DoF. A revolute joint primitive represents a single rotational DoF. A spherical joint primitive represents three rotational DoFs in angle-axis form. A weld joint primitive represents zero DoFs.

■ **degree of ramming**

the extent of hardness to which a sand mould is rammed.

■ **dehumidifying**

is the process of removing moisture from atmospheric air.

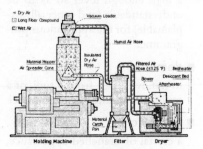

■ **delamination**

separation of plies in a laminate due to adhesive failure. This may be local or may cover a large area. Also includes the separation of layers of fabric from the core structure.

■ **delay screen**

a small piece of perforated light gauge tinned sheet steel, or of copper, aluminium, and/or magnesium alloys, frequently placed in the pouring basin at the top of the downsprue. It delays the flow of metal long enough to allow the basin to fill before it melts to permit only clean metal from the bottom of the basin to enter the downsprue. Delay screens are also use elsewhere in the gating system.

■ **delayed combustion**

a continuation of combustion beyond the furnace.

■ **deliberative control:**

deliberative control architectures use internal, symbolic representations such as maps, models, and knowledge bases to make decisions and mediate actions. These classical AI (Artificial Intelligence) decision processes are structured at a high enough level so as to be understandable (and especially explainable) for the applications programmer.

■ **demould**

to remove a part from a tool, or a tool from an intermediate model.

■ **dendrite**

a crystal of branched appearance, formed during solidification of alloys, the branching habit being controlled by specific crystallographic directions.

■ **denier**

numbering system for continuous yarn and continuous filaments in which the yarn number is equal to the weight in grams per 9,000 meters of yarn; the finer the yarn, the lower the denier.

■ **densitometer**

instrument utilising the photoelectric principle to determine the degree of darkening of developed photographic film.

■ **density**

mass per unit volume. Common units are kilograms per cubic meter (SI metric), grams per cubic centimeter (CGS metric), pounds per cubic foot (British).

■ **density (photographic)**

density is used to denote the degree of darkening of photographic film. Logarithm of opacity of exposed and processed film. Opacity is the reciprocal of transmission; transmission is the ratio of transmitted to incident intensity.

■ **dephosphorisation**

elimination of phosphorus from molten steel.

■ **dermatis**

an inflammation of the skin, which may be caused by allergy to certain casting adjuncts, as resins; particularly in the shell process.

descale

remove the fire scale from the surface of casting.

design allowable

limiting value for a material property that can be used to design a structural or mechanical system to a specified level of success with a specific level of statistical confidence.

design base line

the noise spectrum which is the goal of any particular noise reduction program.

design load

the load for which a steam generating unit is designed, considered the maximum load to be carried.

design pressure

the pressure used by engineers to calculate part thickness and heat exchanger design. It is generally slightly higher than the most severe condition or highest operating pressures seen by the heat exchanger. Also called Maximum Allowable Operating Pressure.

design steam temperature

the temperature of steam for which a boiler is designed.

designations

type of metal named, as steel, malleable, non-ferrous, etc.

despersion hardening

hardening by the formation of hard microconstituents dispersed in a softer matrix.

desulphurisation

removal of sulphur from the molten metal by addition of suitable compounds.

desulphuriser

a material used to remove sulphur from molten metals and alloys. Also, a form of holding ladle or basin in which the molten metal and desulphurising material are brought into contact.

detroit cup test

a cupping test for sand, using a steel ball as plunger, the depth of cup being shown on a dial.

deviation

the amount of variance.

Devries test

a test to give the relative hardness of deep hardening steels.

dew point

the temperature at which moist air will become saturated and conden-

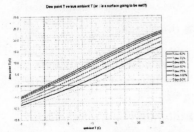

Dew point T versus ambient T (or : is a surface going to be wet?)

sation of water vapour will take place.

dewaxing

the process of melting out the expendable was pattern from an investment mould by the application of heat, usually at temperatures less than 250°F (121)°C).

■ dew-point temperature

is defined as the temperature at which condensation begins when the air is cooled at constant pressure.

■ deoxidation

removal of excess oxygen from molten metal, usually accomplished by adding materials with a high affinity for oxygen, the oxides of which are either gaseous or readily form slags.

■ dextrin

soluble gummy carbohydrate formed by the decomposition of starch by heat, acids, or enzymes; it is use din core compounds, mould compounds, mould washes, core pastes, and other compounds requiring high dry compressive strengths.

■ diagnostic

information indicating the nature or location of a malfunction.

■ diameters

in microscopy, an indication of the amount of magnification. 1000 diameters=1000 times original size.

■ diammonium phosphate

used to fireproof clothing of foundry workers.

■ diaphragm

a flexible material used to separate the control medium from the controlled medium and which actuates the valve stem.

■ diaphragm motor

a diaphragm actuator comprised of case, diaphragm, plate, spring, stem extension, yoke, spring seat, spring adjustor, travel indicator and scale, and handwheel operator.

■ diaphragm pressure span

the difference between high and low values of a diaphragm pressure range.

■ diaphragm shell moulding machine

an arrangement for applying a squeeze pressure with a high-temperature silicone rubber diaphragm.

■ diaspore clay

a rocklike mineral consisting chiefly of diaspore ($HAlO_2$) bonded by fire clay substance with an alumina content higher than 63%.

■ dia-tester (Wolpert hardness tester)

a hardness testing machine using the Vickers or Brinell ball indenter.

■ diathermometer

an instrument for examining the thermal resistance or the heat conducting power of objects.

■ **diatomaceous earth (infusorial earth)**

a hydrous of silica which is soft, light in weight and consists mainly of microscopic shells of diatoms or other marine organisms.

■ **die**

a metal block used in forming materials by casting, moulding, stamping, threading, or extruding.

■ **die assembly**

the parts of a die stamp or press that hold the die and locate it for the punches.

■ **die casting (pressure die casting)**

a rapid, water-cooled permanent mould casting process limited to non-ferrous metals. There are three types: the plunger-type operated hydraulically, mechanically or by compressed air with or without a gooseneck; the direct-air injection which forces metal from a goose-neck into the die, and the Cold-Chamber Machine. All force the metal into the die with a pressure greater than that of gravity flow.

■ **die coating**

see **release agent**.

■ **die insert**

a removable liner or part of a die body or punch.

■ **die set**

in stamping, the parts of the press that hold the die and locate it in proper relation to the punches.

■ **die sinking**

forming or machining a depressed pattern in a die.

■ **dielectric**

nonconductor of electricity; the ability of a material to resist the flow of an electric current.

■ **dielectric oven (dryer)**

a rapid-drying high frequency electric oven used to bake cores.

■ **diesel cycle**

is the ideal cycle for compress-ignition reciprocating engines, and was first proposed by Rudolf Diesel in the 1890s. Using the air-standard assumptions, the cycle consists of four internally reversible processes:
1-2 Isentropic compression.
2-3 Constant pressure heat addition.
3-4 Isentropic expansion.
4-1 Constant volume heat rejection.

■ **Dietert process**

a patented process for the production of precision moulds involving blowing a contoured core around a pattern to form half a mould.

■ **Dietert tester**

a patented apparatus for the direct reading of a Brinell hardness after impression without using magnification or conversion tables.

■ **differential**

the difference between two values of a measured quantity, generally the difference between the highest and lowest values of the quantity. Also called the delta of the quantity.

■ **differential cooling**

occurs when one area of the part cools at a different rate or when the mould surfaces are at different temperatures. Warping results from differential cooling.

■ **differential heat treatment**

a heating process by which the temperature is varied within the object so that, after cooling, various parts may have different properties as desired.

■ **differential operators**

a Gaussian kernel and its derivatives at several scales is a complete basis for information conveyed in a spatial or temporal signal. Elements of this set focus on edges or curvatures etc., and are used to identify particular features in appearance-based models of the signal.

■ **diffuser**

x-ray equipment, a portion of the condensing and focusing system that permits even distribution of energy.

■ **diffuser efficiency**

is a measure of a diffuser's ability to increase the pressure of the fluid. It is expressed in terms of the ratio of the kinetic energy that can be converted to pressure rise if the fluid is discharged at the actual exit stagnation pressure to the maximum kinetic energy available for converting to pressure rise. These two quantities are iden-

tical for an isentropic diffuser since the actual exit stagnation pressure in this case becomes equal to the inlet stagnation pressure, yielding an efficiency of 100 percent.

■ **dike**

a patented flexible seal to prevent blow-by in core boxes.

■ **dilatometer**

an instrument for measuring the length of a metal sample during heating and cooling.

■ **dimensional stability**

retention of the precise shape of the cavity.

■ **dimensional tolerance grades**

a system of classifying the tightness of tolerances for the purpose of defining accurately the tolerances involved, and for simplifying the communication process between customer and producer regarding what is wanted, and what is possible, respectively.

■ **dimensionally homogeneous**

means that every term in an equation must have the same unit. To make sure that all terms in an engineering equation have the same units is the simplest error check one can perform.

■ **dimensions**

are any physical characterisations of a quantity.

■ **dip coat**

in solid and shell mould investment casting, a fine ceramic coating applied as a slurry to the pattern to produce maximum surface smoothness, followed by a cheaper conventional investment.

■ **dip tank**

a tank, preferably lined with rubber, epoxy, or other non-metallic, into which diecastings are dipped for cooling after leaving the machine.

■ **dipped joint**

a thin joint made by dipping of the brick in a thin mortar.

■ **direct actuator**

a diaphragm actuator in which the actuator stem extends as diaphragm pressure increases.

■ **direct casting**

teeming from the ladle into the casting mould without the use of a tundish.

■ **direct numerical control (DNC)**

the use of a computer for providing data inputs to several remote numerically controlled machine tools.

■ **direct-acting instrument**

an instrument in which the air pressure supplied to a controlled device increases as the quantity being measured by the instrument increases.

■ **direct-acting valve**

a normally open valve which requires fluid pressure to close it.

■ **direct-arc furnace**

an electric arc furnace in which the metal being melted is one of the poles.

■ **directionality**

the directionality of a joint, constraint, or driver is its direction of forward motion. The joint directionality is set by the order of the joint's connected bodies and the direction of the joint axis vector. One body is the base body, the other the follower body. The joint direction runs from base to follower, up to the sign of the joint axis vector. Reversing the base-follower order or the joint axis vector direction reverses the forward direction of the joint. Joint directionality sets the direction and the positive sign of all joint position/angle, motion, and force/torque data. Directionality of constraints and drivers is similar, except there is no joint axis, only the base-follower sequence.

■ **dirt trap**

a well employed in a gating system to entrap the first metal poured, which may contain dirt or unwanted particles (ineffective). See Slag Trap.

■ dirty casting

a casting containing an excessive amount of non-metallic inclusions in the body of the metal.

■ DIS

see **Ductile Iron Society** for address.

■ disappearing filament pyrometer

a telescope in which a hot body is viewed through an eyepiece; temperature is measured by the matching colour of a calibrated lamp filament with colour of hot metal.

■ disassembled joint

a disassembled joint need not respect the assembly tolerance of your machine.

For a disassembled prismatic primitive, the Body coordinate system (CS) origins do not have to lie on the prismatic axis. The Bodies translate relatively along misaligned axes.

For a disassembled revolute primitive, the Body CS origins do not have to be collocated. The Bodies rotate relatively about misaligned axes.

The a disassembled spherical primitive, the Body CS origins do not have to be collocated. The Bodies pivot relatively about these two dislocated origins.

You can only use disassembled joints in a closed loop, with no more than one per loop.

■ disbond

unplanned non-adhered or unbonded area within a bonded interface. Can be caused by adhesive or cohesive failure, may occur at any time during the life of the structure and may arise from a wide variety of causes. The term is also sometimes used to describe a delamination.

■ discharge coefficient

a parameter that is used to express the performance of a nozzle, is defined as the ratio of the mass flow rate through the nozzle to the mass flow rate through the nozzle for isentropic flow from the same inlet state to the same exit pressure.

■ discrete-event dynamic systems

abbreviated as DEDS. A DEDS framework models the Behaviour of a continuous process in terms of discrete events observed at run-time. Axioms in a DEDS specification can be used to prove that certain discrete events can't occur by limiting the set of admissible control actions. Using these tools, control decisions can be focused on safe and relevant actions while learning to construct policies for Behaviour. This is one of the ways that autonomous learning machines can be directed to acquire important control knowledge.

■ disengaging surface

the surface of the boiler water from which steam is released.

■ dispersed shrinkage

small shrinkage cavities dispersed through the casting, which are not necessarily cause for rejection.

■ **displacement volume**

is the volume displaced by the piston as it moves between top dead centre and bottom dead centre.

■ **dissociation**

the process by which a chemical compound breaks down into simpler constituents, as do CO_2 and H_2O at high temperature.

■ **dissolved carbon**

carbon in solution in steel in either the liquid or solid state.

■ **dissolved solid**

those solids in water which are in solution.

■ **distillate fuels**

liquid fuels distilled usually from crude petroleum.

■ **distillation**

vapourisation of a substance with subsequent recovery of the vapour by condensation. Often used in less precise sense to refer to vapourisation of volatile constituents of a fuel without subsequent condensation.

■ **distilled water**

water produced by vapourisation and condensation with a resulting higher purity.

■ **distorted pattern**

a pattern untrue to the specified dimensions.

■ **distortion**

see **warpage**.

■ **distribond**

a siliceous clay containing Bento-

nite used as bond in moulding sands.

■ **distributed impact test**

in impingement erosion testing, an apparatus or method that produces a spatial distribution of impacts by liquid or solid bodies over an exposed surface of a specimen. Notes Examples of such tests are those employing liquid sprays or simulated rainfields. If the impacts are distributed uniformly over the surface, the term "uniformly distributed impact test" may be used.

■ **distribution, sand grain**

variation or uniformity in particle size of a sand aggregate when properly screened.

■ **distributive flow**

divided into three categories.

■ **distruptive strength**

maximum strength of a metal when subjected to three principal tensile stresses at right angles to one another and of equal magnitude.

■ **disturbed metal**

the cold worked metal formed on a polished surface during the processes of grinding and polishing.

■ **divorced pearlite**

pearlite in which the cementite has been spheroidised by prolonged annealing just below the Ac1 point, or by annealing at the same temperature after cold working.

■ **DoF**

a degree of freedom (DoF).

dolomite

a mineral calcium-magnesium carbonate $(CaMg(CO_3)_2)$ used as a flux in iron melting and smelting; also as a base in refractors.

dome

the name of a type of nozzle connection. A dome provides a larger nozzle opening between the customer's pipe size and heat exchanger tube bundle, usually to prevent tube erosion due to high inlet velocities.

dominant flow

at the juncture of two confronting flows the dominant flow will reverse the direction of the other.

dose

a quantity of radiation measured at a certain point expressed in roentgens, rems or rads.

dose meter, integrating

ionisation chamber and measuring system designed for determining total radiation administered during an exposure. In medical radiology the chamber is usually designed to be placed on the patient's skin. A device may be included to terminate the exposure when it has reached a desire value.

dose rate

dose per unit time.

dose, exposure

quantity of radiation measured in air in roentgens without backscatter at a given point.

dosimeter

instrument used to detect and measure an accumulated dosage of radiation; in common usage it is a pencil-size ionisation chamber with a built-in self-reading electrometer; used for personal monitoring.

dosimeter, pocket

a pocket ionisation chamber containing it own electrometer. An auxiliary charging device is usually necessary.

double annealing

as applied to hypoeutectoid steel, a process of heating to above the upper critical point (Ac3) and holding at that temperature until complete solution of the carbide has been achieved then cooling rapidly and reheating immediately to above A3 and slowly cooling.

double impression method

a way of determining approximate Brinell hardness by placing a hardened steel ball between a specimen of known hardness and the metal to be tested and pressurising in an arbor press.

double skin

a defect consisting of a secondary layer of metal sometimes found on top-poured ingots.

double tempering

a retempering operation sometimes necessary for steel containing retained austenite which breaks down during cooling from the first tempering to form a new and hence untempered martensite.

doublebruned

deadburn; not to be mistaken for

two firing.

■ **doubler**

extra layers of reinforcement for added stiffness or strength in laminate areas that incur abrupt load transfers.

■ **dowel**

1. a wooden or metal pin of various types used in the parting surface of parted patterns and core boxes
2. in diecasting dies, metal pins to ensure correct registry of cover and ejector halves.

■ **downcomer**

1. a tube or pipe in a boiler or waterwall circulating system through which fluid flows downward.
2. in air pollution control, a pipe for conducting bases down into a conditioner and subsequent cleaning.

■ **downgate**

see **downsprue**.

■ **downhand welding**

welding deposited along a horizontal line and surface.

■ **downsprue**

the first channel, usually vertical, which the molten metal enters; so called because it conducts metal down into the mould.

■ **downtime**

amount of time a piece of equipment is not operational.

■ **draft**

the negative pressure (vacuum) at a given point inside the heater, usually expressed as inches of water, relative to atmospheric pressure outside the heater at the same elevation.

■ **draft differential**

the difference in static pressure between two points in a system.

■ **draft gauge**

a device for measuring draft, usually in inches of water.

■ **draft, pattern**

see pattern draft.

■ **drag**

lower or bottom section of a mould or pattern.

■ **drain**

a valved connection at the lowest point for the removal of all water from the pressure parts.

■ **drape**

the ability of prepreg to conform to the shape of a contoured surface.

■ **draw**

a term used to temper, to remove pattern from mould, or an external contraction defect on surface of mould.

■ **draw peg**

a wooden peg used for drawing patterns.

■ **draw plate**

a plate attached to a pattern to facilitate drawing of a pattern from the mould.

■ **draw screw**

a threaded rod with an eye screwed

into a pattern to enable it to be drawn from the mould.

draw spike

a steel spike used to rap and draw a pattern from the sand; it is driven into the wood of the pattern, as opposed to a Draw Screw, which threaded.

drawback

part of a mould of green sand that may be drawn back to clear over-hanging portions of the patterns.

drawing

removing pattern from the mould or mould from pattern in production work.
See also Temper.

dried sand

sand which bas been dried by mechanical dryer prior to use in core making.

drier (dryer)

a material, as alcohol ammonium nitrate, sodium perborate and manganese oleate, added to a core or mould mixture to remove or reduce the water content.

drillings, test

chips, or small particles of metal removed from a test specimen for chemical analysis.

drive

the part of the robot that supplies power to move. It is the 'engine' that moves the links— sections between the joints— into their desired position. Most drives are powered by air, hydraulics, or elec-tricity.

driver

a constraint that restricts degrees of freedom as an explicit function of time (a rheonomic constraint) and independently of any applied forces/torques. A driver removes one or more independent degrees of freedom, unless that driver is inconsistent with the applied forces/torques and leads to a simulation error.

drop (dropout)

a casting defect caused by sand dropping from the cope or other overhanging section.

drop ball

a heavy weight, usually ball or pear shaped, dropped from a height to break large pieces of metal scrap. Also used to strengthen warp cast-ings.

drop gate

a term for a pouring gate or run-ner leading directly into the top of the mould.

drop off or drop out

sand falling from the Cope of a mould.
See **drop**.

drop size-

the diameter of a liquid drop if it is approximately spherical; other-wise, the approximate shape and appropriate dimensions must be described.
Notes: In a spray or rainfall, there will normally be a spectrum of drop sizes, which can be presented by distribution curves or histo-grams, showing either number of

drops, or combined volume of drops, as a function of drop size. A representative drop size for a distribution is afforded by the sauter mean diameter, or else by the size interval containing the largest total volume.

■ **drop, liquid**

see **liquid drop**.

■ **drum**

a cylindrical shell closed at both ends designed to withstand internal pressure.

■ **drum ladle**

a cylindrical refractory-lined ladle that is completely enclosed. A removable cover at the pouring spout permits addition of molten metal.

■ **drum, magnetic**

an electrically energised pulley or drum used for removing magnetic materials from sand, non-ferrous borings and turnings, etc.

■ **dry air**

air with which no water vapour is mixed. This term is used comparatively, since in nature there is always some water vapour included in air, and such water vapour, being a gas, is dry.

■ **dry analysis**

a term applied to spectrographic analysis.

■ **dry and baked compression test**

an AFS test to determine the maximum compressive stress that a baked sand mixture is capable of developing.

■ **dry gas**

gas containing no water vapour.

■ **dry pan**

a grinding machine of heavy rollers or millers testing on a bed. Screens or slits allow fine material to pass through.

■ **dry permeability**

the property of a moulded mass of sand bonded or unbonded, dried at 220-230°F (105-110°C) and cooled to room temperature that allows passage of gases resulting during pouring of molten metal into a mould.

■ **dry sand casting**

the process in which the sand moulds are dried at above 212°F (100°C) before using.

■ **dry sand core**

see **core**.

■ **dry sand mould**

a mould from which the moisture has been removed by heating.

■ **dry steam**

steam containing no moisture. Commercially dry steam containing not more than one half of one percent moisture.

■ **dry strength, or dry bond strength**

the maximum compressive, shear, tensile, or transverse strength of a sand mixture which has been dried at 220 to 230°F (105 to 110°C) and cooled to room temperature.

■ **dry winding**

a filament-winding operation in which resin is not used.

■ **dryback boiler**

firetube boiler with a refractory lined back door. Door opens to allow maintenance and/or inspection.

■ **dry-bulb temperature**

is the ordinary temperature of atmospheric air.

■ **dryer, core**

see **core driers**.

■ **dryer, dielectric**

see **dielectric oven**.

■ **dry-gas loss**

the loss representing the difference between the heat content of the dry exhaust gases and their heat content at the temperature of ambient air.

■ **dual cycle**

is the ideal cycle which models the combustion process in both gasoline and diesel engines as a combination of two heat-transfer processes, one at constant volume and the other at constant pressure.

■ **dual metal centrifugal casting**

centrifugal castings produced by pouring a different metal into the rotating mould after the first metal poured.

■ **duct**

a passage for air or gas flow.

■ **ductile erosion behaviour**

erosion behaviour having characteristic properties that can be associated with ductile fracture of the exposed solid surface; i.e., considerable plastic deformation precedes or accompanies material loss from the surface which can occur by gouging or tearing or by eventual embrittlement through work hardening that leads to crack formation. (See also brittle erosion Behaviour.)

Notes: In solid impingement, two easily observable aspects of erosion help to distinguish ductile erosion Behaviour, The first is the manner in which volume removal varies with the angle of attack, ductile materials show maximum volume removal for angles of about 20° to 30°, in contrast to near 90° for brittle erosion behaviour. A second indication of ductile Behaviour is the characteristic ripple pattern that forms on the exposed surface at low values of angle of attack.

■ **dust**

small solid particles created by the breaking up of larger particles by an process.

■ **dynamic temperature**

is the kinetic energy per unit mass divided by the constant pressure specific heat and corresponds to the temperature rise during the stagnation process.

■ **dynamic torque**

turning force exerted on a valve stem due to fluid flow through the valve, and its effect on the closure element.

■ **dynamics**

a forward dynamic analysis of a mechanical system specifies:
1. the topology of how bodies are connected
2. the degrees of freedom (DoFs) and constraints among DoFs
3. all the forces/torques applied to the bodies
4. the mass properties (masses and inertia tensors) of the bodies
5. the initial condition of all DoFs:
6. initial linear coordinates and velocities
7. initial angular coordinates and velocities

The analysis then solves Newton's laws to find the system's motion for all later times.
Inverse dynamics is the same, except that the system's motion is specified and the forces/torques necessary to produce this motion are determined.
Dynamics is distinguished from kinematics by explicit specification of applied forces/torques and body mass properties.

■ **EEROM**

Electronically Erasable Programmable Read Only Memory.

■ **economiser**

utilises waste heat by transferring heat from flue gases to warm incoming feedwater.

■ **eddy current testing**

the detection of discontinuities by observation of the interaction between electromagnetic fields and metals.

■ **edge gate**

entrance to the part from the runner located on the parting line.

■ **EDR**

Equivalent direct radiation is the rate of heat transfer from a radiator or convector. It is equivalent to the square feet of surface area necessary to transfer heat at the same rate at which it is produced by a generator. A single boiler horsepower equals 140 ft^2 EDR.

■ **efficiency**

is one of the most frequently used terms in thermodynamics, and it indicates how well an energy conversion or transfer process is accomplished.

■ **efficiency of a cooking appliance**

can be defined as the ratio of the useful energy transferred to the food to the energy consumed by the appliance.

■ **efficiency of a water heater**

is defined as the ratio of the energy delivered to the house by hot water to the energy supplied to the water heater.

■ **efficiency of resistance heaters**

is 100 percent as they convert all the electrical energy they consume into heat.

■ **e-glass**

denotes 'electrical glass,' so called because of its high electrical resistivity. Refers to borosilicate glass fibres most often used in conventional polymer matrix composites.

■ **ejector**

a device which utilises the kinetic energy in a jet of water or other fluid to remove a fluid or fluent material from tanks or hoppers.

BASEPUMP EJECTOR
WITH SUCTION AND
DISCHARGE TUBING

■ **ejector pin**

part kick-out mechanism.

■ **elastic limit**

maximum stress that a material will withstand without permanent deformation.
See **yield strength**.

■ **elasticity**

the property of materials to recover immediately their original size and shape when load is removed after deformation.

■ **electric boiler**

a boiler in which electric energy is used as the source of heat.

■ **electric motor actuator**

a valve operator in which an elec-

tric gear motor is the major component.

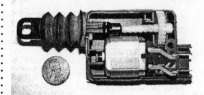

■ **electrical precipitator**

in air pollution control, the use of electrodes in stack emissions emitting high voltage; particles 0.1 micron and smaller can be attached and collected at discharge electrode.

■ **electrical work**

is work done on a system as electrons in a wire move under the effect of electromotive forces while crossing the system boundary.

■ **electrochemical corrosion**

also known as contact corrosion, electrolytic corrosion, Galvanic corrosion. Localised corrosion from exposure of an assembly of dissimilar metals in contact or coupled with one another, i.e., electrochemical action.

■ **electrode**

compressed graphite or carbon cylinder or rod used to conduct electric current in electric arc furnaces, arc lamps, carbon arc welding, etc.

■ **electron microprobe analyser**

an instrument for selective analysis of a microscopic area, in which an electron beam bombards the point of interest in vacuum at a given energy level. Intensity of backscatter is measured to interpret which chemical elements are present, and by scanning a large area the microprobe can Analyse chemical composition and indicate the distribution of an element.

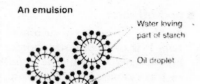

An emulsion

Water loving part of starch

Oil droplet

■ **electro-pneumatic actuator**

a valve operator having an electrical control system that transduces the electrical signal of a controller into a pneumatic input to the diaphragm housing.

■ **electrostatic precipitator**

a device for collecting dust, mist or fume from a gas stream, by placing an electrical charge on the particle and removing that particle onto a collecting electrode.

■ **element**

a triangle defined by three nodes, creating the basis for the finite element analysis.

■ **elongation**

the fractional increase in length of a material loaded in tension. When expressed as a percentage of the original length, it is called percent elongation.

■ **embrittlement**

loss of ductility of a metal due to chemical or physical change. See Acid Embrittlement and Hydrogen Embrittlement.

■ **emulsion**

a mixture of oil and water that does not readily separate.

■ **encoder**

an electronic device used to measure small units of motion, often using a light source and detector.

■ **end**

general term for a continuous, ordered assembly of essentially parallel, collimated filaments, with or without twist.

■ **end effecter**

the tool or gripper which is attached to the mounting surface of the manipulator wrist in order to perform the robot's task.

■ **end of flow**

the melt is just touching the last part of the mould to be filled and the pressure at that point is zero.

■ **end plate**

end plates are covers which have been welded to the heat exchanger. Most end plates are used on bonnet assemblies.

■ **end zone**

the first baffle space on a tube bundle. It is the space between the tubesheet and the first baffle plate. The end zone is adjusted to keep the baffle plates within the two shell side nozzles.

end-effector

the 'hand' connected to the robot's arm. It is often different from a human hand - it could be a tool such as a gripper, a vacuum pump, tweezers, scalpel, blowtorch - just about anything that helps it do its job. Some robots can change end-effectors, and be reprogrammed for a different set of tasks. If the robot has more than one arm, there can be more than one end-effector on the same robot, each suited for a specific task.

end-of-arm tooling

virtually anything that is placed on the end of a robot arm.

endothermic reaction

the reaction which occurs with absorption of heat.

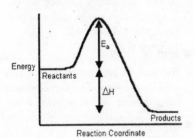

Reaction Coordinate

end-quench hardenability test

a standardised method for comparing the hardenability of different steels.

energy efficiency rating

(EER) is the performance of refrigerators and air conditioners, and is the amount of heat removed from the cooled space in Btu's for 1 Wh (watt-hour) of electricity consumed.

energy transport by mass

is the product of the mass of the flowing fluid and its total energy. The rate of energy transport by mass is the product of the mass flow rate and the total energy of the flow.

engineering strain (e)

the average linear strain, obtained by dividing the elongation of the length of the specimen by the original gauge length.

engineering stress (s)

the load divided by the original area.

English system

which is also known as the United States Customary System (USCS), has the respective units the pound-mass (lbm), foot (ft), and second (s). The pound symbol lb is actually the abbreviation of libra, which was the ancient Roman unit of weight.

enthalpy

H (from the Greek word enthalpien, which means to heat) is a property and is defined as the sum of the internal energy U and the PV product.

$$A-B + C-D \longrightarrow A-C + B-D$$
$$H_{reactants} \qquad\qquad H_{products}$$

$$\triangle H = H_{products} - H_{reactants}$$

enthalpy departure

is the difference between the enthalpy of a real gas and the enthalpy of the gas at an ideal gas state and it represents the variation of the enthalpy of a gas with pressure at a fixed temperature.

■ **enthalpy departure factor**

is the non-dimensionalised form of the enthalpy departure. Entropy departure is the difference between the entropy of a real gas at a given P and T and the entropy of the gas at an ideal gas state at the same P and T .

■ **enthalpy of a chemical component**

at a specified state is the sum of the enthalpy of formation of the component at 25°C, 1 atm, and the sensible enthalpy of the component relative to 25°C, 1 atm, which is the difference between the sensible enthalpy at the specified state ad the sensible enthalpy at the standard reference state of 25°C and 1 atm. This definition enables us to use enthalpy values from tables regardless of the reference state used in their construction.

■ **enthalpy of combustion**

H_C is the enthalpy of reaction during a steady-flow combustion process when 1 kmol (or 1 kg) of fuel is burned completely at a specified temperature and pressure and represents the amount of heat released.

■ **enthalpy of formation**

is the enthalpy of a substance at a specified state due to its chemical composition. The enthalpy of formation of all stable elements (such as O_2, N_2, H_2, and C) has a value

of zero at the standard reference state of 25°C and 1 atm.

■ **enthalpy of reaction**

h_R is defined as the difference between the enthalpy of the products at a specified state and the enthalpy of the reactants at the same state for a complete reaction.

■ **enthalpy of vaporisation**

(or latent heat of vapourisation) is the quantity H_{fg} listed in the saturation tables.

■ **entrainment**

the conveying of particles of water or solids from the boiler water by the steam.

■ **entropy**

(from a statistical thermodynamics point of view) can be viewed as a measure of molecular disorder, or molecular randomness. The entropy of a system is related to the total number of possible microscopic states of that system, called thermodynamic probability p, by the Boltzmann relation, expressed as $S = k \ln p$ where k is the Boltzmann constant.

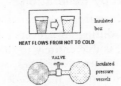

HEAT FLOWS FROM HOT TO COLD

GAS FLOWS FROM HIGH TO LOW PRESSURE

CLASSICAL EXAMPLES OF ENTROPY INCREASE

■ **entropy balance relation for a control volume**

is stated as the rate of entropy

change within the control volume during a process is equal to the sum of the rate of entropy transfer through the control volume boundary by heat transfer, the net rate of entropy transfer into the control volume by mass flow, and the rate of entropy generation within the boundaries of the control volume as a result of irreversibilities.

■ **entropy balance relation in general**

is stated as the entropy change of a system during a process is equal to the net entropy transfer through the system boundary and the entropy generated within the system as a result of irreversibilities.

■ **entropy change of a closed system**

is due to the entropy transfer accompanying heat transfer and the entropy generation within the system boundaries.

■ **entropy departure factor**

is the non-dimensionalised form of the entropy departure.

■ **entropy generation**

S_{gen} is entropy generated or created during an irreversible process, is due entirely to the presence of irreversibilities, and is a measure of the magnitudes of the irreversibilities present during that process. Entropy generation is always a positive quantity or zero. Its value depends on the process, and thus it is not a property.

■ **environment**

refers to the region beyond the immediate surroundings whose properties are not affected by the process at any point.

■ **epc (expendable pattern casting)**

see **lost foam process**.

■ **epoxy**

thermoset polymer containing one or more epoxide groups, curable by reaction with amines or other compounds.

■ **EPROM**

Electronically Programmed Read Only Memory.

■ **equal percentage characteristics**

for low flow control and start-up procedures, heavy increasing often requires larger valve sizes.

■ **equal percentage plug**

a valve plug shaped to allow flow of a medium in direct proportion to the amount of plug lift.

■ **equaliser**

connections between parts of a boiler to equalise pressures.

■ **equation of state**

is any equation that relates the pressure, temperature, and specific volume of a substance. Property relations that involve other properties of a substance at equilibrium states are also referred to as equations of state.

■ **equilibrium**

implies a state of balance. In an

equilibrium state there are no unbalanced potentials (or driving forces) within the system. A system in equilibrium experiences no changes when it is isolated from its surroundings.

equilibrium constant

for an equilibrium reaction is the ratio of the product of the product component's partial pressure raised to their stoichiometric coefficients and the product of the reactant component's partial pressure raised to their stoichiometric coefficients. The equilibrium constant of an ideal-gas mixture at a specified temperature can be determined from knowledge of the standard-state Gibbs function change at the same temperature. The number of equilibrium constant relations needed to determine the equilibrium composition of a reacting mixture is equal to the number of chemical species minus the number of elements present in equilibrium.

equivalence ratio

is the ratio of the actual fuel-air ratio to the stoichiometric fuel-air ratio.

equivalent ellipsoid

the equivalent ellipsoid of a body is the homogeneous solid ellipsoid, centred at the body's centre of gravity, with the same principal moments of inertia and principal axes as the body. A homogeneous solid ellipsoid is the simplest body with three distinct principal moments.

Every body has a unique equivalent ellipsoid, but a given homogeneous ellipsoid corresponds to an infinite number of other, more complicated, bodies. The rotational dynamics of a body depend only on its equivalent ellipsoid (which determines its principal moments and principal axes), not on its detailed shape.

equivalent evaporation

evaporation expressed in pounds of water evaporated from a temperature of 212 °F to dry saturated steam at 212 °F.

ergonomics

the science which deals with the interaction between people, their work place and environment. It also considers the physiology of workers in the design of tools, equipment, and the work methods needed.

Ericsson cycle

is made up of four totally reversible processes:
1-2 T = constant expansion (heat addition from the external source).
2-3 P = constant regeneration (internal heat transfer from the working fluid to the regenerator).
3-4 T = constant compression (heat rejection to the external sink).
4-1 P = constant regeneration (in-

ternal heat transfer from the regenerator back to the working fluid).

■ **erosion**

in tribology, progressive loss of original material from a solid surface due to mechanical interaction between that surface and a fluid, a multi-component fluid, or impinging liquid or solid particles, Notes: Because of the broad scope of this term, it is recommended that it normally be qualified to indicate the relevant mechanism or context, for example, cavitation erosion, liquid impingement erosion, solid impingement erosion, beach erosion, etc.

■ **erosion rate**

any determination of the rate of loss of material (erosion) with exposure duration. (See also **rationalised erosion rate**.)
Notes Erosion rate is usually determined as a slope on the cumulative erosion-time curve. Since in cavitation or liquid impingement this curve is generally not a straight line, it is necessary to specify how any particular numerical value was determined from this curve. The following more explicit terms may be used: **average erosion rate, instantaneous erosion rate, interval erosion rate, maximum erosion rate, and terminal erosion rate**. See individual definitions of these terms.

■ **erosion rate-time curve**

a plot of instantaneous erosion rate versus exposure duration, usu-ally obtained by numerical or graphical differentiation of the cumulative erosion-time curve. (See also **erosion rate-time pattern**.)

■ **erosion rate-time pattern**

any qualitative description of the shape of the erosion rate-time curve in terms of the several stages of which it may be composed.
Notes: In cavitation and liquid impingement erosion, a typical pattern may be composed of all or some of the following 'periods' or 'stages': incubation period, acceleration period, maximum-rate period, deceleration period, terminal period, and occasionally catastrophic period. The generic term 'period' is recommended when associated with quantitative measures of its duration, etc.; for purely qualitative descriptions the term 'stage' is preferred.

■ **erosion-corrosion**

a synergistic process involving both erosion and corrosion, in which each of these processes is affected by the simultaneous action of the other, and in many cases is thereby accelerated.

■ **etchant**

a solution for chemically etching the polished surface of a metal specimen to reveal macro- or micro-structures.

■ **Euler angles**

a representation of a three-dimensional spherical rotation as a product of three successive independent rotations about three independent axes by three independent (Euler) angles.

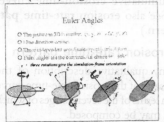

eutectic

1. an isothermal reversible reaction in which a liquid solution decomposes, on cooling, into two or more intimately mixed solids. The number of solids formed are the same as number of components in the system.
2. an alloy having the chemical composition indicated by the eutectic point on a equilibrium diagram.

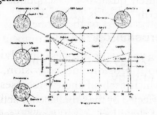

eutectoid

1. an isothermal reversible reaction in which a solid solution on cooling is converted into two or more intimately mixed solids. The number of solids formed are the same number of components in the system.
2. an alloy having the same chemical composition indicated by the eutectoid point on a equilibrium diagram.

evaporation

the change of state from a liquid to a vapour.

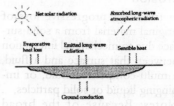

evaporation pattern casting

see lost foam process.

evaporation rate

the number of pounds of water that is evaporated in a unit of time.

evaporative coolers

also known as swamp coolers, use evaporative cooling based on the principle that as water evaporates, the latent heat of vapourisation is absorbed from the water body and the surrounding air. As a result, both the water and the air are cooled during the process.

evaporator

is a heat exchanger in which the working fluid evaporates as it receives heat from the surroundings.

■ **excess air**

the percentage of air in the heater in excess of the theoretical (stochiometric) amount required for combustion.

■ **executive memory**

the portion of memory holding the executive program.

■ **executive program**

the basic operating instructions for a robot placed in memory at the factory.

■ **exergy (availability or available energy)**

is property used to determine the useful work potential of a given amount of energy at some specified state. It is important to realise that exergy does not represent the amount of work that a work-producing device will actually deliver upon installation. Rather, it represents the upper limit on the amount of work a device can deliver without violating any thermodynamic laws.

■ **exergy balance**

can be stated as the exergy change of a system during a process is equal to the difference between the net exergy transfer through the system boundary and the exergy destroyed within the system boundaries as a result of irreversibilities (or entropy generation).

■ **exergy balance for a control volume**

is stated as the rate of exergy change within the control volume during a process is equal to the rate of net exergy transfer through the control volume boundary by heat, work, and mass flow minus the rate of exergy destruction within the boundaries of the control volume as a result of irreversibilities.

■ **exergy destroyed**

is proportional to the entropy generated and is expressed as $X_{destroyed} = T_0 S_{gen}$. Irreversibilities such as friction, mixing, chemical reactions, heat transfer through a finite temperature difference, unrestrained expansion, non-quasi-equilibrium compression, or expansion always generate entropy, and anything that generates entropy always destroys exergy.

■ **exergy of the kinetic energy**

(work potential) of a system is equal to the kinetic energy itself regardless of the temperature and pressure of the environment.

■ **exergy of the potential energy**

(work potential) of a system is equal to the potential energy itself regardless of the temperature and pressure of the environment.

■ **exergy transfer by heat**

x_{heat} is the exergy as the result of heat transfer Q at a location at absolute temperature T in the amount of $X_{heat} = (1-T_0/T)Q$.

■ **exergy transfer by work**

is the useful work potential expressed as $X_{work} = W - W_{surr}$ for closed systems experiencing boundary work where $W_{surr} = P_0(v_2 - v_1)$ and P_0 is atmospheric pressure, and V'_1 and V'_2 are the initial and final volumes of the system, and $X_{work} = W$ for other forms of work.

■ **exergy transport by mass**

results from mass in the amount of m entering or leaving a system and carries exergy in the amount of $m\ae$, where $\ae = (h - h_0) - T_0(s - s_0) + V^2/2 + g\tilde{z}$ accompanies it. Therefore, the exergy of a system increases by $m\ae$ when mass in the amount of m enters, and decreases by the same amount when the same amount of mass at the same state leaves the system.

■ **exhaust valve**

is the exit through which the combustion products are expelled from the cylinder.

■ **exotherm**

heat released during a chemical reaction. Uncontrolled exotherm can lead to extreme heat build up and possibly violent explosion.

■ **exothermic**

formed by or characterised by heat reaction as in oxidation.

■ **exothermic reaction**

chemical reactions involving the liberation of heat.

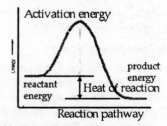

See **endothermic reaction**.

■ **expansion joint**

the joint to permit movement due to expansion without undue stress.

■ **experiment**

a test to answer a question or illustrate a point, usually conducted under controlled conditions. Also an action, as in 'to experiment.'

■ **explorer**

a person who travels to a distant place in search of new information and discovery.

■ **explosion door**

a door in a furnace or boiler setting that is designed to be opened by a pre-determined gas pressure.

■ **exposure duration**

in erosion or wear, exposure time, or any other appropriate measure of the accumulation of exposure to an erosion or wear environment.

Notes: For impingement erosion, some alternative duration parameters are the number of impacts that have occurred on a given point, or the mass or volume of particles that have impinged on a unit area of exposed surface. For wear, it may be the sliding distance travelled.

■ **ex-proof exd**

pressure resistant capsuled.

■ **ex-proof exi**

intrinsically safe.

■ **extended surface**

surface added to the outside of bare tubes in the convection section to provide more heat transfer area.

This usually consists of fins or studs welded to the tube.

■ **extensive properties**

are those whose values depend on the size or extent of the system. Mass m, volume V, and total energy E are some examples of extensive properties.

■ **extensometer**

an instrument used in the testing of metals to measure small increments of deformation.

■ **external combustion engines**

are engines in which the fuel is burned outside the system boundary.

■ **external sensor**

a feedback device for detecting locations, orientations, forces, or shapes of objects outside of the robots immediate surroundings.

■ **external treatment**

treatment of boiler feed water prior to its introduction into the boiler.

■ **externally reversible**

process has no irreversibilities to occur outside the system boundaries during the process. Heat transfer between a reservoir and a system is an externally reversible process if the surface of contact between the system and the reservoir is at the temperature of the reservoir.

■ **fabric**

planar textile. Also known as cloth.

■ **fabric, non-woven**

planar textile constructed by bonding or interlocking, but not interlacing, by mechanical, chemical, thermal or solvent means.

■ **fabric, woven**

planar textile constructed by interlacing in a weaving process.

■ **fabrication**

1. the joining, usually by welding, of two or more parts to produce a finished assembly. The components of the assembly may be a combination of cast and wrought materials.

2. process of making a composite part or tool.

■ **facing sand**

specially prepared moulding sand mixture used in the mould adjacent to the pattern to produce a smooth casting surface.

■ **Fahrenheit scale**

(named after the German instrument maker G. Fahrenheit, 1686-1736) is the temperature scale in the English system. On the Fahrenheit scale, the ice and steam points are assigned 32 and 212 °F.

■ fail safe valve

a valve that either fails in the open position or closes to prevent a costly or dangerous situation within a system.

■ false brinelling

damage to a solid bearing surface characterised by indentations not caused by plastic deformation resulting from overload but thought to be due to other causes such as jetting corrosion. (See also brinelling.)

■ family mould

a mould which produces non-identical parts simultaneously.

■ fan

a machine consisting of a rotor and housing for moving air or gases at relatively low pressure differentials.

■ fan performance

a measure of fan operation in terms of volume, total pressures, static pressures, speed, power input, mechanical and static efficiency, at a stated air density.

■ fan performance curves

the graphical presentation of total pressure, static pressure, power input, mechanical and static efficiency as ordinates and the range of volumes as abscissa, all at constant speed and air density.

■ fanno line

is the locus of all states for frictionless adiabatic flow in a constant-area duct plotted on a T-S diagram.

■ fatigue

failure or deterioration of a material's mechanical properties as a result of repeated cyclic loading or deformation over time.

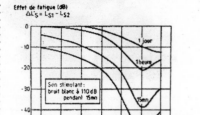

■ fatigue crack or failure

a fracture starting from a nucleus where there is an abnormal concentration of cyclic stress. The fracture surface is smooth and frequently shows concentric (sea shell) markings with a nucleus as a centre.

■ fatigue limit (endurance limit)

maximum stress that a material will endure without failure for an infinite number of load cycles.

■ fatigue strength

maximum cyclical stress withstood for a given number of cycles before a material fails. The residual strength after being subjected to fatigue loading.

■ fatigue wear

wear of a solid surface caused by fracture arising from material fatigue.

■ FEA

finite-element analysis.

■ feed pump

a pump that supplies water to a boiler.

■ feedback

a signal from the robot equipment about conditions as they really exist, rather than as the computer has directed them to exist.

■ feedback controller

a mechanism which measures the value of a controlled variable, compares it to a command or set value, and manipulates a controlled system in order to maintain a desired relationship between controlled variable and command.

■ feedback loop

a signal orientating in the computer that is changed by the robot and given back as feedback.

■ feedback signal

the signal which is returned to the input of a system and compared to a reference signal to establish an actuated signal which returns the controlled variable to the desired value.

■ feeding

the process of supplying molten metal to compensate for volume shrinkage while the casting is solidifying.

■ feedwater

water introduced into a boiler during operation. It includes make-up and return condensate.

■ feedwater heater

is the device where the feedwater is heated by regeneration. This technique is used to raise the temperature of the liquid leaving the pump (called the feedwater) before it enters the boiler. A practical regeneration process in steam power plants is accomplished by extracting, or 'bleeding,' steam from the turbine at various points. This steam, which could have produced more work by expanding further in the turbine, is used to heat the feedwater instead.

■ feedwater treatment

the treatment of boiler feed water by the addition of chemicals to prevent the formation of scale or to eliminate other objectionable characteristics.

■ ferrite

a solid solution of one or more elements in the body-centre-cubic phase of iron or steel.

■ ferritic steels

steels in which ferrite is the predominant phase. These steels are magnetic.

■ ferromagnetic

the ability to become highly magnetic and have the ability to retain a permanent magnetic moment. The elementary magnetic dipoles inside the domainz are all oriented alike.

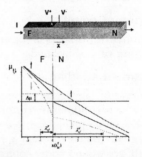

■ ferrule

a small piece of tubing approximately 1 inch long made of copper or stainless steel. The ferrule is crimped or squeezed onto the tie tube, up against the last baffle, thus locking all the baffles into position.

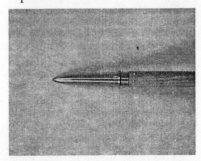

■ fettle

British term meaning the process of removing all runners and risers and cleaning off adhering sand from the casting. Also refers to the removal of slag from the inside of the cupola and in Britain to repair the bed of an open hearth.

■ FGR

Flue Gas Recirculation or the recirculation of flue gas with combustion air to reduce NO_x emissions.

■ fibre

one or more filaments in an ordered assemblage.

■ fibre architecture

design of a fibrous preform or part in which the fibres are arranged (braided, stitched, woven, etc.) in a particular way to achieve the desired result.

■ fibre content

amount of fibre present in a composite expressed either as a percent by weight or percent by volume. Also sometimes stated as a fibre volume fraction.

■ fibre optics

the use of thin strands of flexible glass to transmit light around corners.

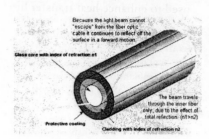

Because the light beam cannot "escape" from the fiber optic cable it continues to reflect off the surface in a forward motion.

Glass core with index of refraction n1

The beam travels through the inner fiber only, due to the effect of total reflection. (n1>n2)

Protective coating

Cladding with index of refraction n2

fibre orientation

direction of fibre alignment in a non-woven or mat laminate wherein most of the fibres are placed in the same direction to afford greater strength in that direction.

fibre placement

continuous process for fabricating composite shapes with complex contours and/or cutouts by means of a device that lays preimpregnated fibres (in tow form) onto a non-uniform mandrel or tool. Differs from filament winding in several ways: There is no limit on fibre angles; compaction takes place online via heat, pressure or both; and fibres can be added and dropped as necessary. The process produces more complex shapes and permits a faster putdown rate than filament winding.

fibre volume fraction

see **fibre content**.

fibre-reinforced plastics (FRP)

general term used for a polymer-matrix composite that is reinforced with cloth, mat, strands or any other fibre form. Often used to designate mid-range, glass-fibre reinforced composites.

filament

polycrystalline or amorphous individual fibre unit with a length-to-diameter ratio greater than one. The minimum diameter of a filament is not limited, but the maximum diameter may not exceed 0.010 inches. Filaments greater than about 0.002 inches in diameter are often referred to as wires.

filament count

number of filaments in the cross-section of a fibre bundle.

filament winding

process of fabricating composites in which continuous reinforcing fibres, either preimpregnated with resin or drawn through a resin bath, are wound under controlled tension around a rotating form to make a structure. (See also **winding, mandrel**.)

fill

fibre bundles in a woven fabric that run transverse to the warp yarns; also known as weft or woof.

fill pattern

the contours of the advance of the material as the cavity fills.

fill pressure

the pressure required to fill the cavity.

filler

solid constituent, usually inert, added to the matrix to modify the composite properties such as increase viscosity, improve appearance or lower density, or to lower cost.

■ **filler ply**

additional patch to fill in a depression in repair or to build up an edge.

■ **fillet**

a concave corner piece used on foundry patterns, a radius joint replacing sharp inside corners.

■ **film**

a thin fluid layer adjacent to a pipe wall, which remains in laminar flow, even when the bulk flow is turbulent.

■ **film adhesive**

adhesive in the form of a thin, dry resin film with or without a carrier; commonly used for adhesion between laminate layers.

■ **film coefficient**

the convective heat transfer coefficient of the film.

■ **film temperature**

the maximum temperature in the film, at the tube wall.

■ **filter**

porous material through which fluids or fluid and solid mixtures are passed to separate matter held in suspension.

■ **fin**

a fin is an extended surface, a solid, experiencing energy transfer by conduction within its boundaries, as well as energy transfer with its surroundings by convection and/or radiation, used to enhance heat transfer by increasing surface area.

■ **fin tube**

a tube with one or more fins.

■ **finish**

material applied to textiles to improve the bond between the fibre and matrix; applied after sizing is removed.

■ **finish allowance**

the amount of stock left on the surface of a casting for machining.

■ **finish mark**

a symbol (f, f1, f2, etc.) appearing on the line of a drawing that represents the edge of the surface of the casting to be machined or otherwise finished.

■ **finish welding**

production welding carried out in order to ensure the agreed quality of the casting.

■ **finite difference analysis (fda)**

a computerised numerical modelling approach for solving differential equations. Used primarily in solving heat transfer and solidification problems.

■ **finite element analysis**

the solution of simultaneous equations for each element (triangle) with resulting pressure, temperature and elapsed time at each node and the direction and speed of the material (at the instant of fill).

■ fire box

a term used to describe the structure, which houses the radiant tubes and the burners .

■ firecracker core

see pencil core.

■ fired pressure vessel

a vessel containing a fluid under pressure exposed to heat from the combustion of fuel.

■ firetube

a type of boiler design in which combustion gases flow inside the tubes and water flows outside the tubes.

TYPE 302PC

■ firing rate control.

a pressure temperature or flow controller which controls the firing rate of a burner according to the deviation from pressure or temperature set point. The system may be arranged to operate the burner on-off, high-low or in proportion to load demand.

■ first law of thermodynamics

is simply a statement of the conservation of energy principle, and it asserts that total energy is a thermodynamic property. Joule's experiments indicate the following: For all adiabatic processes between two specified states of a closed system, the net work done is the same regardless of the nature of the closed system and the details of the process.

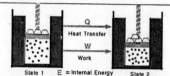

First Law of Thermodynamics

State 1   E = Internal Energy   State 2
$$E_2 - E_1 = Q - W$$

Any thermodynamic system in an equilibrium state possesses a state variable called the internal energy (E). Between any two equilibrium states, the change in internal energy is equal to the difference of the heat transfer into the system and work done by the system.

■ first law of thermodynamics for a closed system

using the classical thermodynamics sign convention is $Q_{net, in} - W_{net, out} = \Delta E_{system}$ or $Q - W = \Delta E$ where $Q = Q_{net, in} = Q_{in} - Q_{out}$ is the net heat input and $W = W_{net, out} = W_{out} - W_{in}$ is the net work output. Obtaining a negative quantity for Q or W simply means that the assumed direction for that quantity is wrong and should be reversed.

■ fixed carbon

the carbonaceous residue less the ash remaining in the test container after the volatile matter has been driven off in making the proximate analysis of a solid fuel.

■ **fixed tubesheet**

a non-removable tubesheet. The tubesheet on a core assembly. Any tubesheet that is an integral part of the shell assembly.

■ **flame**

a luminous body of burning gas or vapour.

■ **flame detector**

a device which indicates if a fuel (liquid, gaseous, or pulverised) is burning, or if ignition has been lost. The indication may be transmitted to a signal or to a control system.

■ **flame hardening**

a surface hardening process involving localised flame heating to above the austenite transformation temperature, Ac3, followed by quenching.

■ **flame propagation rate**

speed of travel of ignition through a combustible mixture.

■ **flame safeguard**

a control that sequences the burner through several stages of operation to provide proper air purge, ignition, normal operation, and shutdown for safe operation.

■ **flammability**

susceptibility to combustion.

■ **flange**

a rim on the end of a valve, pipe or fitting for bolting onto another pipe element.

■ **flanges din 25..**

these flanges always fit to butt-welded ends DIN 26.. on the pipelines.

■ **flash**

a thin section of metal formed at the mould, core, or die joint or parting in a casting due to the cope and drag not matching completely or where core and coreprint do not match.

■ **flash point**

the lowest temperature at which, under specified conditions, fuel oil gives off enough vapour to flash into a momentary flame when ignited.

■ **flashing**

the process of producing steam by discharging water into a region of pressure lower than the saturation pressure that corresponds to the water temperature.

■ **flask**

a metal frame used for making or holding a sand mould. The upper part is the cope and the bottom half is the drag.

■ flask bar

a reinforcing member attached within either half of a flask to assist in holding the rammed sand in position.

■ flask clamp

a device for holding together the cope, drag, and cheek of a flask.

■ flask pin guides

guides used to accurately align the match plate pattern in the flask and flask to flask location.

■ flat back

a pattern with a flat surface at the joint of the mould. It lies wholly within the drag and the joint of the cope is a plane surface.

■ flexibility

the ability of a robot to perform a variety of different tasks.

■ flexural modulus

ratio, within the elastic limit, of the applied stress on a test sample in flexure to the corresponding strain in the outermost fibres of the sample.

■ flexural strength

strength of a material in bending, usually expressed in force per unit area, as the stress of a bent test sample at the instant of failure.

■ flip-flop

a logic element that will give one of two signals each time it is stimulated, alternating between the two.

■ floating tubesheet

the tubesheet at one end of a removable tube bundle. The floating tubesheet will always have a smaller diameter than the stationary. The floating tubesheet is allowed to move freely with the expansion and contraction of the tube bundle due to temperature changes in operation.

■ floppy disk

a small flexible disk used to record computer information.

■ flow balancing

modifying flow paths, particularly runner sections, so that all flow paths within a mould fill in equal time with equal pressure.

■ flow cavitation

cavitation caused by a decrease in static pressure induced by changes in velocity of a flowing liquid. Typically, this may be caused by flow around an obstacle or through a constriction, or relative to a blade or foil. A cavitation cloud or "cavitating wake" generally trails from some point adjacent to the obstacle or constriction to some distance downstream, the bubbles being formed at one place and collapsing at another.

■ **flow coefficient**

the number of gallons of water per minute at 60°F (16° C) that will flow through a valve with a pressure drop of one pound per square inch. It is also referred to as the C_v (K_v) of a valve.

■ **flow deflector**

local reduction in thickness to divert flow.

■ **flow leader**

local increase in thickness to encourage flow in a particular direction.

■ **flow pattern**

the contour the melt takes sequentially as it fills the cavity. The mould should fill with a straight flow front with no changes in direction throughout filling.

■ **flow rate**

the volume of material passing a fixed point per unit time.

■ **flow work, or flow energy**

is work required to push mass into or out of control volumes. On a unit mass basis this energy is equivalent to the product of the pressure and specific volume of the mass Pv.

■ **flow, laminar**

a condition of flow in which fluid moves in parallel layers. It occurs in situations where the Reynolds number is less than approximately 2000.

■ **flow, turbulent**

a flow condition in which the fluid moves in a random manner. It generally occurs when the Reynolds number is greater than approximately 4000.

■ **flow-control valves**

valves that can change the rate of flow to equipment.

■ **flowmeter**

a device which is used to indicate either flow rate, total flow or a combination of both.

■ **flow-off (pop-off)**

a large vent, usually located at the high of the mould cavity. In addition to letting air and mould gases escape as metal fills the mould cavity, the flow-off fills with metal and acts to relieve the surge of pressure near the end of the pouring.

■ **flue**

a passage for products of combustion.

flue gas

a mixture of gaseous products resulting from combustion of the fuel. Forced Draft Use of a fan to supply combustion air to the burners of a heater and to overcome the pressure drop of the burners and any air preheat equipment.

fluid

the state of matter that is not solid and is able to flow and change shape. The term fluid includes both the liquid state and the gas or vapour state.

fluidity

the ability of molten metal to flow. Common devices used to measure fluidity are: spiral casting and the Chinese Puzzle.

fluidise

to impart fluid like properties to powders or sands e.g. fluidised beds.

fluorescing

to give off very bright light when shone on by light.

FM

factory Mutual.

foaming

the continuous formation of bubbles which have sufficiently high surface tension to remain as bubbles beyond the disengaging surface.

follower (follower body)

the point to which the joint is directed. The joint directionality runs from base to follower body. Joint directionality sets the direction and the positive sign of all joint position/angle, motion, and force/torque data.

force sensor

a device that measures and detects the magnitude of the force exerted by an object upon contacting.

forced circulation

the circulation of water in a boiler by mechanical means external to the boiler.

forced-draft cooling tower

or induced-draft cooling tower, is a wet cooling tower in which the air is drawn through the tower by fans.

forced-draft fan

a fan supplying air under pressure to the fuel burning equipment.

formal sign convention

(classical thermodynamics sign convention) for heat and work interactions is as follows: heat transfer to a system and work done by a system are positive; heat transfer from a system and work done on a system are negative.

fouling

the accumulation of refuse in gas passages or on heat absorbing surfaces which results in undesirable restriction to the flow of gas or heat.

foundry returns

metal in the form of sprues, gates, runners, risers and scrapped castings, with known chemical composition that are returned to the furnace for remelting. Sometimes referred to as 'revert'.

■ **four-stroke**

internal combustion engines are engines in which the piston executes four complete strokes (two mechanical cycles) within the cylinder, and the crankshaft completes two revolutions for each thermodynamic cycle.

■ **four-way pilot valve**

a pilot valve used with double acting actuators.

■ **fracture**

rupture of the surface of a laminate due to external or internal forces; may or may not result in complete separation.

■ **fracture toughness**

measure of the damage tolerance of a material containing initial flaws or cracks.

■ **free ash**

ash which is not included in the fixed ash.

■ **freeze off -**

the temperature of the material is reduced to the point that it blocks an area it would fill if it were hotter.

■ **fretting-**

in tribology, small amplitude oscillatory motion, usually tangential, between two solid surfaces in contact.
Notes Here the term fretting refers only to the nature of the motion without reference to the

wear, corrosion, or other damage that may ensue. The term fretting is often used to denote fretting corrosion and other forms of fretting wear. Usage in this sense is discouraged due to the ambiguity that may arise.

■ **fretting corrosion**

a form of fretting wear in which corrosion plays a significant role.

■ **fretting wear**

wear arising as a result of fretting (see **fretting**).

■ **friction force**

the resisting force tangential to the interface between two bodies when, under the action of an external force, one body moves or tends to move relative to the other. (See also **coefficient of friction**.)

■ **frictional heating**

heat generated by the friction of the chains of molecules slipping past each other.

■ **frictional wear**

the displacement and/or detachment of metallic particles from a surface as a consequence of being in contact with another moving component.

■ **froth flow**

used to describe mist or annular mist flow regimes.

■ **froude number**

used in hydraulics as an analogue to the Reynolds number. It is the ratio of inertial forces to gravitational forces.

■ **FRP**

fibre-reinforced plastic.

■ **fuel**

a substance containing combustible used for generating heat.

■ **fuel cells**

operate on the principle of electrolytic cells in which the chemical energy of the fuel is directly converted to electric energy, and electrons are exchanged through conductor wires connected to a load. Fuel cells are not heat engines, and thus their efficiencies are not limited by the Carnot efficiency. They convert chemical energy to electric energy essentially in an isothermal manner.

■ **fuel oil**

a liquid fuel derived from petroleum or coal.

■ **fuel-air mixture**

mixture of fuel and air.

■ **fuel-air ratio**

the ratio of the weight, or volume, of fuel to air.

■ **fuel-to-steam efficiency**

the ratio of heat added to boiler feedwater to produce the output steam to the amount of energy inputted with fuel.

■ **furnace**

an enclosed space provided for the combustion of fuel.

■ **furnace pressure**

pressure occurring inside the combustion chamber; positive if greater than atmospheric, negative if less than atmospheric, and neutral if equal to atmospheric.

■ **furnace volume**

the cubic contents of the furnace or combustion chamber.

■ **fusible plug**

a hollow threaded plug having the hollow portion filled with a low melting point material.

■ **gauge length**

the original length of that portion of the specimen over which strain or change of length is determined.

■ **gauge marks**

reference marks; in tensile testing, the marks which indicate the gauge length, used in determination of tensile elongation.

■ **gauge pressure**

is the difference between the absolute pressure and the local atmospheric pressure.

■ **gaggers**

metal pieces of irregular shape used to reinforce and support the sand in the mould.

■ **gauging**

checking dimensional requirement by means of a gauge.

■ **galling**

a form of surface damage arising between sliding solids, distinguished by macroscopic, usually localised, roughening and creation of protrusions above the original surface; it often includes plastic flow or material transfer or both. Notes: The onset of galling usually requires that the contact pressure exceeds some threshold value. Galling can be a precursor to seizing or loss of function. The identification of galling is somewhat subjective, and complete agreement does not exist, even among experts.

■ **gamma iron**

a face-centred cubic form of pure iron, stable from 1670 to 2551°F (910 to 1400°C).

■ **gannister**

an acid (silicious) refractory often used in furnace linings.

■ **gas analysis**

the determination of the constituents of a gaseous mixture.

■ **gas burner**

a burner that uses gas or fuel.

■ **gas constant**

R is different for each gas and is determined from $R = Ru/M$.

■ **gas phase of a substance**

has molecules that are far apart from each other, and a molecular order is non-existent. Gas molecules move about at random, continually colliding with each other and the walls of the container they are in.

■ **gas power cycles**

are cycles where the working fluid remains a gas throughout the entire cycle. Spark-ignition automobile engines, diesel engines, and conventional gas turbines are familiar examples of devices that operate on gas cycles.

■ **gas pressure regulator**

a spring loaded, dead weighted or

pressure balanced device which will maintain the gas pressure to the burner supply line.

■ gas refrigeration cycle

is based on the reversed Brayton cycle where the compressor exit gases are cooled and then expanded in a turbine to further reduce the temperature of the working fluid. The lower-temperature fluid is used to produce the refrigeration effect.

■ gasket

a material used for sealing a joint in a piping system. It usually is a flat piece of elastomer, cork, asbestos compound or similar material and is used between mating flanges or similar surfaces. It provides a static permanent seal.

■ gate

the narrowed link between the runner and the cavity.

■ gate valve

a valve in which a sliding disc or gate is moved by an actuator perpendicular to the direction of flow. They are normally used in the fully opened or fully closed position and not for throttling purposes.

■ gating system

the complete assembly of sprues, runners and gates in a mould through which steel flows before entering the casting cavity.

■ gauge

an instrument used for measuring some physical property such as pressure, temperature, etc.

■ gauge cock

a valve attached to a water column or drum for checking water level.

AL   SB

■ gauge glass

the transparent part of a water gauge assembly connected directly or through a water column to the boiler, below and above the water line, to indicate the water level in a boiler.

■ gauge pressure

the pressure above atmospheric pressure.

■ gear meshing

the placing of two gears so that there teeth will fit together without interference.

■ gel time

period of time from initial mixing of liquid reactants to the point when gelation occurs as defined by a specific test method.

■ **generalised compressibility chart**

shows that by curve-fitting all the data, gases seem to obey the principle of corresponding states reasonably well.

■ **generalised enthalpy departure chart**

is a plot of the enthalpy departure factor as a function of reduced pressure and reduced temperature. It is used to determine the deviation of the enthalpy of a gas at a given P and T from the enthalpy of an ideal gas at the same T.

■ **generalised entropy departure chart**

is a plot of the entropy departure factor as a function of reduced pressure and reduced temperature. It is used to determine the deviation of the entropy of a gas at a given P and T from the entropy of an ideal gas at the same P and T.

■ **generator**

is a device that converts mechanical energy to electrical energy.

■ **generator efficiency**

is the ratio of the electrical power output to the mechanical power input.

■ **geothermal heat pumps**

(also called ground-source heat pumps) use the ground as the heat source.

■ **Gibb's function**

g is defined as $g = h - Ts$.

■ **Gibb's phase rule**

provides the number of independent variables associated with a multicomponent, multiphase system.

■ **Gibbs-Dalton law**

an extension of Dalton's law of additive pressures, states that under the ideal-gas approximation, the properties of a gas in a mixture are not influenced by the presence of other gases, and each gas component in the mixture behaves as if it exists alone at the mixture temperature and mixture volume.

■ **gland**

the cavity of a stuffing box into which the packing is stuffed.

■ **gland sealing**

former often used measure for sealing of stuffing box, in modification also grease sealing gland (lubricator) or for control of stuffing box sealing.

■ **glass transition**

reversible change in an amorphous polymer between a viscous condition and a hard, relatively brittle condition.

■ **glass transition -**

change in an amorphous polymer from viscous to hard and relatively brittle.

■ **glass-transition temperature (Tg)**

approximate temperature at which increased molecular mobility results in significant changes in properties of a cured resin. The measured value of T_g can vary, depending on the test method.

■ **globe valve**

a family of valves characterised by a closure member which travels in a line perpendicular to the valve seat. They are used primarily for throttling purposes and general flow control.

■ **gouging abrasion**

abrasion involving gross surface indentation and possible removal of sizable metal fragments.

■ **grade**

oil classification according to quality, generally based on ASTM specifications.

■ **grain fineness number**

a system developed by AFS for rapidly expressing the average grain size of a given sand. It approximates the number of meshes per inch of that sieve that would just pass the sample if its grains of uniform size. It is approximately proportional to the surface area per unit of weight of sand, exclusive of clay.

■ **grains (water)**

a unit of measure commonly used in water analysis for the measurement of impurities in water (17.1 grains = 1 part per million ppm).

■ **grains per cu-ft**

the term for expressing dust loading in weight per unit of gas volume (7000 grains equals one pound).

■ **granular fracture (crystalline fracture)**

a type of irregular surface produced when metal is broken.

■ **graphite fibres**

carbon fibre that has been graphitised by heating and stretching at temperatures above 3,000°F.

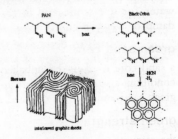

■ **graphitisation**

process of pyrolysis at very high temperatures (up to 5,400°F) that converts carbon to its crystalline allotropic form.

■ **gravimetric analysis**

is one way to describe the composition of a mixture that is accomplished by specifying the mass of each component.

gravitational acceleration

g is 9.807 m/s^2 at sea level and varies by less than 1 percent up to 30,000 m. Therefore, g can be assumed to be constant at 9.81 m/s^2.

gravity

weight index of fuels: liquid, petroleum products expressed either as specific, Baume or A.P.I. (American Petroleum Institute) gravity; weight index of gaseous fuels as specific gravity related to air under specified conditions; or weight index of solid fuels as specific gravity related to water under specified conditions.

green sand

a naturally bonded sand or a compounded moulding sand mixture which has been tempered with water for use while still in the damp or wet condition.

green sand core

a sand core used in the unbaked condition, also a core made from green sand and used as rammed.

green strength

the strength of a tempered sand mixture at room temperature.

gripper

end-of-arm tooling used to grasp objects.

ground

a ground or ground point is a special point fixed at rest in the absolute or global inertial World reference frame. Each ground has an associated grounded coordinate system (CS). The grounded CS's origin is identical to the ground point, and its coordinate axes are always parallel to the coordinate axes of World.

grounded CS

a local CS attached to a ground point. It is at rest in World, but its origin is wherever the ground point is and therefore in general shifted with respect to the World CS origin. The coordinate axes of a grounded CS are always parallel to the World CS axes.
The World coordinate axes are defined so that:
+x points right.
+y points up (gravity in -y direction).
+z points out of the screen, in three dimensions.
You automatically create a grounded CS whenever you set up a ground block.

group technology

the grouping of parts into categories having common characteristics, such as shape, so that all parts within each category can be processed together.

hadfield manganese steel

a specially steel which is austenitic and usually contains approximately 12% Manganese. It is used in mining, earth- moving equipment and in railroad track work.

hall effect switch

a switch that conducts when a magnet is placed close to it.

hand layup

fabrication method in which reinforcement layers, preimpregnated or coated afterwards, are placed in a mould by hand, prior to cure to the formed shape.

■ **handhole**

an access opening in a pressure part usually not exceeding 6" in its longest dimension.

■ **handhole cover**

a handhole closure.

■ **hard automation**

automated machinery that is fixed, or dedicated, to one particular manufacturing task throughout its life.

■ **hard particle erosion,**

deprecated term; use the preferred synonyms solid impingement erosion or solid particle erosion.

■ **hard tool**

tool made of metal or any "hard" material that is generally impervious to damage during normal use.

■ **hard water**

water which contains calcium or magnesium in an amount which requires an excessive amount of soap to form a lather.

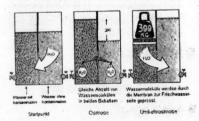

Wasser mit kontamination | Wasser ohne kontamination | Gleiche Anzahl von Wassermolekülen in beiden Behältern | Wassermoleküle werden durch die Membran zur Frischwasserseite gepresst.

Startpunkt | Osmose | Umkehrosmose

■ **hardenability**

in a ferrous alloy, the property that determines the depth and distribution of hardness induced by quenching.

■ **hardener**

substance used to promote or control curing action by participating in and being consumed by the cure reaction.

■ **hardness**

resistance of a material to indentation as measured by such methods as Brinell, Rockwell, and Vickers. The term hardness also refers to stiffness of a material, or its resistance to scratching, abrasion, or cutting.

■ **hard-wired**

a connection made directly with wires rather than through a computer.

■ **harmonic functions**

a formal, potential field approach that is computable using fast numerical techniques, yields the scalar, *hitting probability field*, introduces no local minima, and generates a complete solution up to the resolution of an occupancy grid. Gradient descent on the harmonic potential avoids obstacles and achieves the goal if a path exists.

■ **hazbot**

a robot designed to take the place of a person in a hazardous job, such as repairing nuclear reactors, fighting fires, and exploring planets that are inhospitable to human beings.

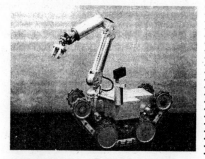

■ **head**

the height of a column of liquid above a specified point expressed in units such as feet of water, inches of mercury, etc. It is a measure of pressure exerted by the column of liquid.

■ **head metal**

the reservoir of metal in the feeder or riser of a mould.

■ **header**

the fittings, which connect two tubes in a coil. In common usage, "header" includes the cast or forged 180 "U-bends" ("Return Bends"). The term is also used to describe collection and distribution manifolds.

■ **header box**

the compartment at the end of the convection section where the headers are located. There is no flue gas flow in the header box, since it is separated from the inside of the heater by an insulated tube sheet.

■ **heat**

term used colloquially to indicate any temperature above ambient

(room) temperature to which a part or material is or will be subjected.

■ **heat available**

the thermal energy above a fixed datum that is capable of being absorbed for useful work.

■ **heat balance**

an accounting of the distribution of the heat input, output and losses.

■ **heat duty**

the total heat absorbed by the process fluid, usually expressed in MMBTU/hr. Total heat duty is the sum of heat transferred to all process streams in the heater, including auxiliary services such as steam generation and steam superheating.

■ **heat engines**

are devices that convert heat to work. Heat engines differ considerably from one another, but all can be characterised by the following:
They receive heat from a high-temperature source (solar energy, oil furnace, nuclear reactor, etc.).
They convert part of this heat to work (usually in the form of a rotating shaft).
They reject the remaining waste heat to a low-temperature sink (the atmosphere, rivers, etc.).
They operate in a cycle.

■ **heat exchangers**

are devices where two moving fluid streams exchange heat without mixing. Heat exchangers are widely used in various industries, and they come in various designs. The simplest form of a heat exchanger is a double-tube (also called tube-and-shell) heat exchanger composed of two concentric pipes of different diameters. One fluid flows in the inner pipe, and the other in the annular space between the two pipes. Heat is transferred from the hot fluid to the cold one through the wall separating them. Sometimes the inner tube makes a couple of turns inside the shell to increase the heat transfer area, and thus the rate of heat transfer.

■ **heat fired**

the total heat released in the fired heater, equal to total fuel fired times the lower heating value (LHV) of the fuel. It is usually expressed in MMBTU/hr.

■ **heat flux**

the rate of heat transfer per unit area is usually based on total outside surface area. Typical units are BTU/hr sq. ft.

■ **heat pump**

is a cyclic device which causes the transfer of heat from a low-temperature region to a high-temperature region. The objective of a heat pump is to maintain the heated space at a high temperature by supplying heat to it.

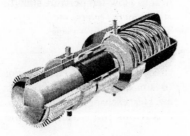

■ **heat pump coefficient of performance**

is the efficiency of a heat pump, denoted by COP_{HP}, and expressed as desired output divided by required input or $COP_{HP} = Q_H / W_{net, in}$.

■ **heat pumps**

are cyclic devices which operate on the refrigeration cycle and discharge energy to a heated space to maintain the heated space at a high temperature.

■ **heat rate**

is the expression of the conversion efficiency of power plants in the United States and is the amount of heat supplied, in Btu's, to generate 1 kWh of electricity. The smaller the heat rate, the greater the efficiency.

■ **heat release rate**

rate that describes the heat available per square foot of heat-absorbing surface in the furnace or per cubic foot of volume.

■ **heat reservoir**

is a thermal energy reservoir since it can supply or absorb energy in the form of heat.

■ **heat sink**

is a heat reservoir that absorbs energy in the form of heat.

■ **heat source**

is a heat reservoir that supplies energy in the form of heat.

■ **heat transfer**

is the area under the process curve on a *T-S* diagram during an internally reversible process. The area has no meaning for irreversible processes.

■ **heat treatment**

a combination of heating and cooling operations and applied to a metal or alloy to produce desired properties and microstructures.

■ **heat-distortion temperature**

temperature at which deflection occurs under specified temperature and stated load.

■ **heat-driven systems**

are refrigeration systems whose energy input is based on heat transfer from an external source. Absorption refrigeration systems are often classified as heat-driven systems.

■ **heater efficiency**

it is the ratio of the heat absorbed to the heat fired.

■ **heating surface**

those surfaces which are exposed to products of combustion on one side and water on the other. This surface is measured on the side receiving the heat.

■ **heating value**

of a fuel is defined as the amount of heat released when a fuel is burned completely in a steady-flow process and the products are returned to the state of the reactants. In other words, the heating value of a fuel is equal to the absolute value of the enthalpy of combustion of the fuel.

■ **heating value of a fuel**

is the amount of heat released when a specified amount of fuel (usually a unit mass) at room temperature is completely burned and the combustion products are cooled to the room temperature.

■ **helical**

ply laid onto a mandrel at an angle, often at a 45° angle.

■ **Helmholtz function**

a is defined as $a = u - Ts$.

■ **Henry's law**

states that the mole fraction of a weakly soluble gas in the liquid is equal to the partial pressure of the gas outside the liquid divided by Henry's constant.

■ **hertzian contact area**

the apparent area of contact between two non-conforming solid bodies pressed against each other, as calculated from Hertz' equations of elastic deformation.

■ **Hertzian contact pressure**

the magnitude of the pressure at any specified location in a Hertzian contact area, as calculated from Hertz' equations of elastic deformation.

■ **hesitation effect**

occurs in parts of varied thicknesses. The flow moves preferentially into a thicker area causing an adjacent thin area to freeze off while the thicker area fills. Gates should be positioned as far as possible from where the flow divides into thick and thin flow paths.

■ **hidden Markov models**

a stochastic model of the process that generated a given sequence of observations. HMMs are finite-state automata with probabilistic state transitions and with a probability distribution over observations from each state. Typical applications involve aspects of pattern recognition, i.e., prediction.

■ **high gas pressure control**

a control to stop the burner if the gas pressure is too high.

■ **high oil temperature control**

a control to stop the burner if the oil temperature is too high.

■ **high pressure mould**

a strong high-density mould, made by air, hydraulic, or other squeeze process.

■ **high stress grinding abrasion**

abrasion that occurs when the abrasive is crushed between two opposing surfaces.

■ **high-alloy steel**

ferrous alloy with more than 12 weight percent of non-carbon additions.

■ **higher heating value**

or HHV, is the heating value of the fuel when the water in the combustion gases is completely condensed and thus the heat of vapourisation is also recovered. Efficiencies of furnaces are based on higher heating values.

■ **high-performance composites**

composites offering properties better than conventional structural metals, typically on a strength-to-weight or stiffness-to-weight basis. Such composites use continuous, oriented fibres in polymer, metal or ceramic matrices to achieve their superior properties.

■ **hindered contraction**

casting contraction during solidification and cooling which is hindered by mould or core restraints.

■ **hollow drill test (trepanning)**

removing a cylindrical sample from a metal section or structure to determine soundness of the section.

■ **homogenising**

a process of heat treatment at high temperature intended to eliminate or decrease chemical segregation by diffusion.

■ **honeycomb**

resin-impregnated material, most commonly manufactured in hexagonal cells, that serves as a core in sandwich structure. May also be a metal or a polymer in rigid, open-cell structure.

■ **hoop**

ply laid onto a mandrel at a 90° angle.

■ **hoop stress**

circumferential stress in a cylindrically shaped part as a result of internal or external pressure.

■ **horizontal axis casting machine**

a centrifugal casting machine in which the axis of rotation of the mould is horizontal.

■ **horsepower**

the unit of power in the British system of units. One horsepower equals 550 ftlb/ sec.

■ **hot box process**

a furan resin-based process similar to shell coremaking; cores produced with it are solid unless mandrelled out.

■ **hot strength (sand)**

tenacity (compressive, shear or transverse) of a sand mixture determined at any temperature above room temperature.

■ **hot tear**

a crack or fracture formed prior to completion of metal solidification as a result of hindered contraction. A hot tear is frequently open to the surface of the casting and is commonly associated with design limitations.

■ **hot-bond repair**

repair made on a hot-patch bonding machine to cure and monitor curing. Typically includes heat and vacuum source.

■ **HSLA**

High Strength Low Alloy Steel. Steel with relatively high strength and impact properties. The carbon level is low and the alloying additions are significantly less than 5 weight percent.

■ **hub**

the cast or forged part of a BCF/ SSCF core assembly. The hub is made up of a tubesheet, shellside nozzle connection and vent/drain connections. The hub eliminates additional welding or brazing operations, therefore, making the exchanger less expensive.

■ **humanoid robotics**

humanoid robotics research includes a rich diversity of projects wherein perception, processing and action are embodied in a recognisably anthropomorphic form in order to emulate some subset of the physical, cognitive and social dimensions of the human body and experience. This work seeks to create a new kind

of tool; fundamentally different from any we have yet seen because it is designed to work with humans as well as for them.

■ **humidifying**

is the process of adding moisture to atmospheric air.

■ **hybrid**

a robot that is part pick and place

and part servo controlled, or has the same abilities.

■ **hybrid composite**

composite containing at least two distinct types of matrix or reinforcement. The matrix or reinforcement types can be distinct because of their physical properties, mechanical properties, material form and/or chemical composition.

▣ **hydraulic cylinder**

a piston in a cylindrical housing, that is moved by pressurised oil.

■ **hydrocarbon**

a chemical compound of hydrogen and carbon.

■ **hydrocarbon fuels**

are the most familiar fuels and consist primarily of hydrogen and carbon. They are denoted by the general formula C_nH_m. Hydrocarbon fuels exist in all phases, some examples being coal, gasoline, and natural gas.

■ **hydrogen embrittlement**

a condition of low ductility resulting from the absorption of hydrogen. A time dependent fracture process which results in a loss of ductility.

■ **hydrostatic test**

a strength and tightness test of a closed pressure vessel by water pressure.

■ **hygroscopic**

readily absorbs moisture.

■ **hypereutectoid steel**

a steel containing more than the eutectoid percentage of carbon (0.83 wt. %).

■ **hypersonic flow**

occurs when a flow has a Mach number $M \gg 1$.

■ **hypoeutectoid steel**

a steel containing less than the eutectoid percentage of carbon (0.83 wt. %).

■ **hysteresis**

in a cyclic process, hysteresis is the failure to follow the same path in the forward direction as in the backward direction.

■ **hysteresis (cooling lag)**

difference between the critical points on heating and cooling due to tendency of physical changes to lag behind temperature changes.

■ **ID grinding**

term for internal (dimension) grinding.

■ **ideal critical diameter, d1**

the largest diameter of a bar which, upon quenching in an ideal quench, will exhibit 50% martensite at the centre of the bar.

■ **ideal critical diameter, di**

the largest diameter of a bar which, upon quenching in an ideal quench, will exhibit 50% martensite at the centre of the bar.

■ **ideal cycle**

is an actual cycle stripped of all the internal irreversibilities and complexities. The ideal cycle resembles the actual cycle closely but is made up totally of internally reversible processes.

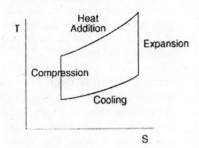

■ ideal gas

is a gas that obeys the ideal-gas equation of state.

■ ideal gas specific heat relation

is $C_p = C_v + R$.

■ ideal gas temperature scale

is a temperature scale that turns out to be identical to the Kelvin scale. The temperatures on this scale are measured using a constant-volume gas thermometer, which is basically a rigid vessel filled with a gas, usually hydrogen or helium, at low pressure.

■ ideal mixture

or ideal solution is a mixture where the effect of dissimilar molecules in a mixture on each other is negligible and the chemical potential of a component in such a mixture is simply taken to be the Gibbs function of the pure component.

■ ideal quench

a quench in which the temperature of an object being quenched instantaneously drops to that of the quench bath and remains constant.

◨ ideal vapour-compression refrigeration cycle

completely vaporises the refrigerant before it is compressed and expands the refrigerant with a throttling device, such as an expansion valve or capillary tube. The vapour-compression refrigeration cycle is the most widely used cycle for refrigerators, air-conditioning systems, and heat pumps. It consists of four processes:
1-2 Isentropic compression in a compressor.
2-3 Constant-pressure heat rejection in a condenser.
3-4 Throttling in an expansion device.
4-1 Constant-pressure heat absorption in an evaporator.

■ ideal-gas equation of state

(or ideal-gas relation) predicts the P-V-T behaviour of a gas quite accurately within some properly selected region where $PV = RT$.

■ ignition

the initiation of combustion.

■ ignition temperature

lowest temperature of a fuel at which combustion becomes self-sustaining.

■ illinois inclusion count method

a determination of the index number of cleanliness of steel.

■ illite

a mineral, typically $KAl_3Si_3O_{10}(OH)_2$, found in many clays, large working of which are found in Illinois and Michigan.

■ illuminants

light oil or coal compounds that readily burn with a luminous flame, such as ethylene, propylene and benzene.

■ immediate surroundings

refer to the portion of the surroundings that is affected by the process.

■ impact angle

in impingement erosion, an angle that could be either the angle of attack or the angle of incidence, which see. Because of this ambiguity, this term should be specially defined when used, or, preferably, used only in contexts where the ambiguity does not matter.

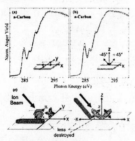

■ impact strength

the resistance to impact loads; usually expressed as the foot pounds of energy absorbed in breaking a standard specimen.
See Charpy Impact Test.

■ impact value

total energy needed to break a standard specimen by a single blow under standard conditions; e.g., Charpy Impact Test.

■ impact velocity

in impingement erosion, the relative velocity between the surface of a solid body and an impinging liquid or solid particle.
Notes: To describe this velocity completely, it is necessary to specify the direction of motion of the particle relative to the solid surface in addition to the magnitude of the velocity. The following related terms are also in use: (1) absolute impact velocity—the magnitude of the impact velocity. (2) normal impact velocity—the component of the impact velocity that is perpendicular to the surface of the test solid at the point of impact.

■ impact wear

wear due to collisions between two solid bodies where some component of the motion is perpendicular to the tangential plane of contact.

■ impingement attack

deprecated term for impingement corrosion. (The latter term is preferred so as to avoid confusion with liquid impingement erosion.)

■ impingement corrosion

a form of erosio corrosion generally associated with the impingement of a high-velocity, flowing liquid containing air bubbles against a solid surface.

■ impingement plate

a small perforated plate or bar assembly placed inside of the shellside nozzle, usually a dome type nozzle. They can also be attached directly to the bundle by being tack welded to the tierods. The impingement plate protects and prolongs the life of the tubes. The impingement plate breaks up and slows down the shellside fluid, which otherwise would erode the tubing.

■ **impingement**

in tribology, a process resulting in a continuing succession of impacts between (liquid or solid) particles and a solid surface.
Notes In preferred usage, "impingement" also connotes that the impacting particles are smaller than the solid surface, and that the impacts are distributed over that surface or a portion of it. If all impacts are superimposed on the same point or zone, then the term "repeated impact" is preferred. In other contexts, the term "impingement" sometimes has different meanings, as in the steady-state impingement of a liquid stream against a solid body, or in "impingement corrosion." The definition given here applies in the context of Committee G-23 scope.

■ **impoverishment**

loss of any constituent from an alloy or from localised areas of an alloy by oxidation, liquidation, volatilisation, or changes in the solid state. The term depletion is also used, particularly in referring to the lowering of the concentration of solute in a solid solution, around particles precipitated from solid solution.

■ **impregnate**

to saturate the voids and interstices of a reinforcement with a resin.

■ **impregnated fabric**

see **prepreg**.

■ **impregnation**

the treatment of castings with a sealing medium to stop pressure leaks, such as soaking under pressure with or without prior evacuation and either with hot or cold application. Mediums used include silicate of soda, drying oils with or without styrene, plastics, and proprietary compounds.

■ **impurity**

an element unintentional allowed in a metal or alloy. Some impurities have little effect on properties; others will grossly damage the alloy.

■ **in and out end**

the end of the heat exchanger which contains the tubeside inlet and outlet connections in a multipass unit.

■ **including 90°**

between a reference direction and the ply principal axis. The ply orientation is positive if measured counterclockwise from the reference direction and negative if measured clockwise.

■ **inclusions**

nonmetallic materials in a metal matrix. Sources include reoxidation, refractories, slag, and deoxidisation products.

■ **incomplete combustion**

is a combustion process in which

the combustion products contain any unburned fuel or components such as C, H_2, CO, or OH.

■ **incompressible substances**

such as liquids and solids, have densities that have negligible variation with pressure.

■ **inconel**

an oxidation-resistant alloy, 80% Ni, 14% Cr, and 6% Fe.

■ **second law of thermodynamics**

the entropy of an isolated system during a process always increases or, in the limiting case of a reversible process, remains constant. In other words, the entropy of an isolated system never decreases.

■ **incremental**

movement broken up into very small pieces, and then taken one at a time.

■ **incubation period**

in cavitation and impingement erosion, the initial stage of the erosion rate-time pattern during which the erosion rate is zero or negligible compared to later stages. Also, the exposure duration associated with this stage. (Quantitatively it is sometimes defined as the intercept on the time or exposure axis, of a straight line extension of the maximum-slope portion of the cumulative erosio time curve.)

■ **indentation hardness**

the resistance of a material to indentation. This is the usual type of hardness test, in which a pointed or rounded indenter is pressed into a surface under a substantially static load. See Brinell Hardness and Hardness.

■ **independent properties**

exist when one property can be varied while another property is held constant.

■ **indestructible**

impossible to break, harm, defeat, or destroy.

■ **indirect-arc furnace**

an AC (Alternating Current) electric-arc furnace in which the metal is not one of the poles.

■ **induced draft**

use of a fan on the flue gas side of the heater to provide additional draft above that supplied by the stack to draw flue gas through the convection section and any other heat recovery equipment.

■ **induced draft fan**

a fan exhausting hot gases from the heat absorbing equipment.

■ **induction furnace**

a AC melting furnace which utilises the heat of electrical induction.

■ **induction hardening**

a surface hardening process involving the localised use of pulsating magnetic currents to achieve heating above the austenite transformation temperature, Ac3, followed by quenching.

■ **induction heating**

process of heating by electrical resistance and hysteresis losses induced by subjecting a metal to the varying magnetic field surrounding a coil carrying an alternating current.

■ **inert gas**

is a gaseous component in a chemical reaction that does not react chemically with the other components. The presence of inert gases affects the equilibrium composition (although it does not affect the equilibrium constant).

■ **inert gaseous constituents**

incombustible gases such as nitrogen which may be present in a fuel.

■ **inertia tensor**

the inertia or moment of inertia tensor of an extended rigid body describes its internal mass distribution and the body's angular acceleration in response to an applied torque.
Let V be the body's volume and ñ(r) its mass density, a function of position r within the body. This inertia tensor is a real, symmetric 3-by-3 matrix or equivalent MATLAB expression.

■ **infrared dryer**

a core or mould dryer employing infrared lamps.

■ **infrared radiation pyrometer**

this instrument which uses the ratio of the radiated energy from a body in two wavelength bands and then is a measure of the body's surface temperature. Temperatures down to 200 C (392 F) may be measured.

■ **infrared rays**

pertaining to or designating those rays which lie just beyond the red end of the visible spectrum, such as are emitted by a hot non-incandescent body. They are invisible and non-actinic and are detected y their thermal effect. Their wave lengths are longer than those of visible light and shorter than those of radio waves. Can be applied in the foundry for drying or core baking operations and for heating dies. Infrared radiant heat are synonymous.

■ **infusorial earth**

a very fine whitish powder composed of the siliceous skeletons of infusorians (Protozoa).

■ **ingates**

the channels through which molten metal enters the mould cavity. See Gate.

■ **ingot**

a mass of metal cast to a convenient size and shape for remelting or hot working.

■ **ingot iron**

iron of comparatively high purity produced in open-hearth furnace under conditions that keep down the carbon, manganese, and silicon content; e.g., Armco Iron.

■ **inhibitor**

a substance which selectively retards a chemical action. An example in boiler work is the use of an inhibitor, when using acid to remove scale, to prevent the acid from attacking the boiler metal.

■ **initial condition actuator**

an *initial condition actuator* gives you a way to move a system's degrees of freedom non-dynamically to prepare a system for dynamical integration, in a way consistent with all constraints.

■ **injection moulding**

the injection of molten metal or other material under pressure into moulds.

■ **injection or fill time**

time required to fill the cavity or mould.

■ **injector**

a device utilising a steam jet to entrain and deliver feed water into a boiler.

■ **inoculant**

material which when added to molten metal modifies the structure, and thereby changes the physical and mechanical properties to a degree not explained on the basis of the change in composition resulting from its use.

■ **inoculation**

addition to molten metal of substances designed to form nuclei for crystallisation.
Also see **inoculant**.

■ **insert -**

a removable part of the mould imparting increased resistance to wear or heat transferability to that area of the mould.

■ **instantaneous erosion rate**

the slope of a tangent to the cumulative erosio time curve at a specified point on that curve.

■ **insulating column**

at medium temperatures below -10°C a corresponding extension depending on the pipeline insulation will be used to protect the stuffing box against freezing.

■ **insulating pads and sleeves**

as opposed to chills, insulating material, such as gypsum, diatomaceous earth, etc., used to lower the rate of solidification. As sleeves on open risers, they are used to keep the metal liquid, thus increasing the feed efficiency.

■ **insulation**

a material of low thermal conductivity used to reduce heat losses.

■ **intake valve**

is an inlet through which the air or air-fuel mixture is drawn into the cylinder.

■ **integral blower**

a blower built as an integral part of a device to supply air thereto.

■ **integral controls**

pertaining to equipment that is supplied and housed or mounted locally with the valve and actuator.

■ **integral dose (volume dose)**

a measure of the total energy absorbed by man or any object during exposure to radiation.

■ **integral heating**

system in which heating elements are built into a tool, forming part of the tool and usually eliminating the need for an oven or autoclave as a heat source.

■ **integral-blower burner**

a burner of which the blower is an integral part.

■ **integrated mounting**

mounting of the positioners to the diaphragm actuators acc. to safety precaution rules (UVV) and especially without complex external piping, susceptible to trouble.

■ **Intelligence**

the ability to make appropriate decisions and take appropriate actions in the face of uncertainty. The word 'appropriate' is best characterised in context, and with reference to the task at hand. For example, some tasks require that appropriate action maximize efficiency while others may emphasize learning, survivability, robustness, or an ability to communicate. Ultimately, intelligence is in the eye of the beholder. "We know it when we see it."

■ **intensity (radiology)**

amount of energy per unit time passing through a unit area perpendicular to the line of propagation at the point in question. Often this term is used incorrectly in the sense of dose rate.

■ **intercast process**

a patented procedure for die casting " cast-assemble " units with moving parts.

■ **intercrystalline failure**

cracks or fractures that follow along the grain boundaries in the microstructure of metals and alloys.

■ **interdendritic attack**

a type of electrochemical corrosion that sometimes occurs in as-cast alloys or alloys that have had very little working.

■ **interface**

a boundary between the robot and machines, transfer lines, or parts outside immediate environment. The root must communicate with these items through input/output signals provided by sensors.

■ **intergranular corrosion**

corrosion in a metal taking place preferentially along the grain boundaries.

■ **interlaminar**

existing or occurring between two or more adjacent laminae in ·a laminate.

■ **interlaminar shear**

shearing force that produces displacement between two laminae along the plane of their interface.

■ **interlock**

a device to prove the physical state of a required condition, and to furnish that proof to the primary safety control circuit.

■ **intermittent blowdown**

the blowing down of boiler water at intervals.

■ intermittent flow

divided into two categories.

■ internal friction

ability of a metal to transform vibratory energy into heat; generally refers to low stress levels of vibration; damping has a broader connotation since it may refer to stresses approaching or exceeding yield strength.

■ internal sensor

a feedback device in the manipulator arm which provides data on the controller on the position of the arm.

■ internal shrinkage

a void or network of voids within a casting caused by inadequate feeding of that section during solidification.

■ internal stresses

generally stresses which occur during the cooling of a part.

■ internal treatment

the treatment of boiler water by introducing chemicals directly into the boiler.

■ interpolation

the process of automatically selecting a path in space based on the positions of the end points of the path; can be used for circular or linear paths.

■ interrupted quench

removing the casting from a quenching bath before it has reached the temperature of the bath.

■ interval erosion rate,

the slope of a line joining two specified points on the cumulative erosio time curve.

■ intralaminar

existing or occurring within a single lamina in a laminate.

■ invar

an alloy having practically no expansion when heated; 36% Ni, 0.5% Mn, 0.2% C, and the balance Fe.

■ inverse segregation

a concentration of certain alloy constituents that have lower melting points in the region corresponding to that first solidifying; caused by interdendritic flow of enriched liquid through channels where the pressure drops with contraction of dendrites. The internal evolution of hydrogen may also give a positive pressure, aiding this flow and causing a liquidated surface as tin sweat.
See also **segregation.**

■ inversion

a change in crystal form without change in chemical composition, as from quartz to cristobalite.

■ inversion casting

1. the metal is fed through a bottom feeder, the mould being inverted for pouring.
2. the mould is directly attached to the electric furnace in which the metal is melted in a reducing atmosphere so no slag is formed. On inverting the furnace the metal runs into the mould. There are no

heavy feeders and oxidation is prevented.

■ **investing**

the process of pouring the investment slurry into the flask surrounding the pattern to form the mould.

■ **investment**

a flowable mixture of a graded refractory filler, a binder and a liquid vehicle which when poured around the patterns conforms to their shape and subsequently set hard to form the investment mould.

■ **investment casting**

casting produced in a mould obtained by investing an expendable pattern with a refractory to produce a shell. The expendable pattern may consist of wax, plastic, or other material and is removed prior to filling the mould with liquid metal.

■ **investment precoat**

an extremely fine investment coating applied as a thin slurry directly to the surface of the pattern to reproduce maximum surface smoothness. The coating is surrounded by a coarser, cheaper, and permeable investment to form the mould.
See Dip Coat.

■ **involute tooth gear**

a circular gear having teeth shaped so as to cause lower friction.

■ **inwall brick**

refractory lining of the inwall section of blast furnace or cupola.

■ **ion**

a charged atom or radical which may be positive or negative.

■ **ionisation**

the process or the result of any process by which a neutral atom or molecule acquires either a positive or a negative charge.

■ **ionisation chamber**

an instrument designed to measure quantity of ionising radiation in terms of the charge of electricity associated with ions produced within a defined volume.

■ **IPS**

abbreviation for the "Iron Pipe Size", used to refer to standard nominal pipe sizes.

■ **iridium**

a noble metal of the platinum group. Used extensively as a radiation source. For radiography of thin walled castings.

■ **iron**

1. a metallic element, mp 1535 C (2795 F)
2. irons not falling into the steel categories, as gray iron, ductile iron, malleable iron, white iron, ingot, and wrought iron.

■ **iron carbide**

see **cementite.**

■ **iron oxide**

this material as prepared for foundry use generally contains about 85% ferric oxide and is produced by pulverizing a high grade of pure iron ore. It can be added to core sand mixes to assist in keeping the core from cracking before the metal solidifies during the casting operation and also helps to resist metal penetration during this period. Added to moulding sand mixtures for control of finning and veining. Also may reduce carbon pick up.

■ **iron sand**

see **iserine.**

■ **iron, hard or white**

irons (Fe3C) possessing white fracture because all or substantially all of the carbon is in the combined form. Irons to be malleablised are cast white, as are many abrasion-resistant irons.

■ **iron, malleable**

a mixture of iron and carbon, including smaller amounts of silicon, manganese, phosphorus, and sulphur, which after being cast (white iron, carbon in combined form as carbides) is converted structurally by heat treatment into a matrix of ferrite containing nodules of temper carbon (graphite).

■ **iron, pearlitic malleable**

a malleable iron having a more or less pearlitic matrix.

■ **iron-carbon (graphite) diagram**

a diagram representing stable equilibrium conditions between iron and graphite (pure carbon) phase over the entire range of iron and steel.

■ **iron-iron carbide diagram**

a phase diagram representing metastable equilibrium conditions between Fe and Fe_3C over the entire range of carbon steels and cast irons.

■ **iserine**

a black sand which consists mainly of magnetic iron ore but also contains a considerable amount of titanium.

■ **ISO**

international Standards Organisation.

■ **isobar**

a line of equal pressure. In mouldflow graphic output, any point along an isobar sees the same cavity pressure as any other point along the same isobar.

■ **isochrone**

a line of equal time. In mouldflow graphic output, any point along an isochrone is filled at the same time as any other point along the same isochrone.

■ **isocure**

proprietary name for a binder system developed for use in Ashland (Cold Box) Process, itself a proprietary process.

■ **isocyanate acid**

isomeric cyanic acid (HNCO).

■ **isomorphous**

phases with crystal structures of the same type.

■ **isotherm**

a line of equal temperature. In mouldflow graphic output, any point along an isotherm is at the same temperature as any other point along the same isotherm.

■ **isothermal**

pertaining to changes or other phenomena occurring at a constant temperature.

■ **isothermal annealing**

a process in which a ferrous alloy is heated to produce a structure partly or wholly austenitic, and is then cooled to and held at a temperature that causes transformation of the Austenite to a relatively soft ferric-carbide aggregate.

■ **isothermal transformation**

1. the process of transforming Austenite in a ferrous alloy to Ferrite or a ferrite-carbide aggregate at any constant temperature within the transformation range
2. transformation of one phase in an alloy system to another phase at any constant temperature.

■ **isotope**

one of several different nuclides having the same number of protons in their nuclei, and hence having the same atomic number, but differing in the number of neutrons and therefore in the mass number.

■ **isotropic**

fibre directionality with uniform properties in all directions, independent of the direction of applied load.

■ **j**

1. symbol for 1 gram equivalent weight
2. the mechanical equivalent of heat.

■ **jack arch**

a spring arch, flat or horizontal on the underside.

■ **jamb**

usually an upright structural member forming the side of an opening in a refractory or furnace wall.

■ **jamb brick**

a brick modified so one corner is rounded.

■ **jar ramming**

packing sand in a mould by raising and dropping on a table the sand, pattern, and flask. Jolt squeezers, jarring machines, and jolt rammers are machines using this principle.

■ **jersey fireclay brick**

highly siliceous clay brick, semisilica brick.

■ **jet scrubber**

in air pollution control, a high velocity water jet directed into the throat of a venture section of a cupola to separate out particulates.

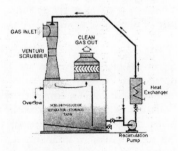

■ **je′ segment**

see liquid jet.

jet tapping

a method of tapping a melting furnace by firing a small explosive charge instead of using an oxygen lance. The tapper consists of an explosive charge enclosed in a plastic case surrounded by a hollow bullet-shaped body.

jet, liquid

see **liquid jet**.

jib

projecting part of crane from which lifting chain or gear is suspended.

jig

any device so arranged that it will expedite a hand or a machine operation.

j-integral

a mathematical expression used to characterise the fracture toughness of a material having appreciable plasticity prior to fracture. The J-integral eliminates the need to describe the Behaviour of the material near the crack tip. Units are MN/m or in in-lb/in^2.

jobbing foundry

a foundry engaged in the manufacture of numerous types of castings.

joint

represents one or more mechanical degrees of freedom between two bodies. Joint blocks connect two Body blocks in a Mechanics schematic. Joints have no mass properties such as mass or an inertia tensor. A *joint primitive* represents one translational or rotational degree of freedom or one spherical (three rotational degrees of freedom in angle-axis form). Prismatic and revolute primitives have motion axis vectors. A weld primitive has no degrees of freedom. A *primitive joint* contains one joint primitive. A *composite joint* contains more than one joint primitive. Joints have a *directionality* set by their base-to-follower Body order and the direction of the joint primitive axis. The sign of all position/angle, motion, and force/torque data is determined by this directionality.

joint welding

production welding used to weld cast components together to obtain an integral unit.

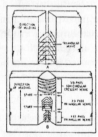

jointed arm robot

a robot whose arm consists of two links connected by 'elbow' and 'shoulder' joints to provide three rational motions. This robot most closely resembles a human arm.

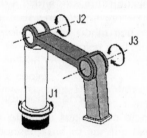

■ **jolt ramming**

see **jar ramming.**

■ **jolt-squeezer machine**

a combination machine that employs a jolt action followed by a squeezing action to compact the sand around the pattern.

■ **k**

symbol used in linear elastic fracture mechanics to describe the intensification of applied stress at the tip of a crack of known size and shape. At the onset of rapid crack propagation, the factor is call the critical stress-intensity factor (KIc) or fracture toughness. Various subscripts denote loading conditions or fracture toughness. Units are Mpa/mm or ksi/in.

■ **k factor**

tensile strength in pounds per square inch divided by the Brinell Hardness number.

■ **kahlbaum iron**

an iron of more than 99.975% purity, produced in Germany.

■ **kalling-dommarfvet process**

a desulphurising process using powdered burnt iron.

■ **kaolin**

the purest form of China clay consisting of silicate of aluminium.

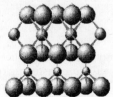

■ **kappa carbide**

a carbide of iron (Fe-2,3; C-6) in which all or part of the iron may be replaced by chromium, molybdenum, and/or tungsten.

■ **kayser hardness test**

a method for determining the true hardness of metals at high temperatures.

■ **kc (plane-stress fracture toughness)**

the value of stress intensity at which crack propagation becomes rapid in sections thinner than those in which plane-strain conditions prevail. Units are MPa/m or ksi/in.

■ **kelvin temperature scale**

one in which the unit of measurement equals that of the centigrade degree and according to which absolute zero is 0 degrees, equivalent to -273.16 C.

■ **kerf**

the width of a cut.

■ **kevlar**

trademark of DuPont for high-performance para-aramid fibres used as reinforcements.

■ **keyhole specimen**

a type of notched impact test specimen which has a hole-and-slot notch shaped like a keyhole.

■ **kic (plane-strain fracture toughness)**

the minimum value of KC. Represents the fracture toughness of a material independent of crack length, or loading system. Units are MPa/m or ksi/in.

■ **kieselguhr**

diatomaceous earth, a finely porous material used for thermal insulation to 1100 °C (2012 °F).

■ **kiln**

an oven or furnace for burning, calcimining or drying a substance.

■ **kiln marks**

irregularities on the surface of refractors caused by deformation under load during burning.

■ **kiln-dried**

lumber artificially dried in a specially designed enclosure or lumber kiln.

■ **kilovolt (kv)**

unit of electrical potential equal to 1,000 volts.

■ **kilovolts constant potential**

the potential in kilovolts of a constant voltage generator.

■ **kilovolts peak**

the crest value of the potential wave in kilovolts. When only one half of the wave is used, the crest value is to be measured on this half of the wave.

■ **kinematic conditioning**

a quality of a particular configuration of an articulated mechanism for transforming input force/velocity to output force/velocity, usually represented in the form of a scalar field. Especially important for redundant mechanisms since there are many ways to accomplish the same task. Here, conditioning metrics can be used to amplify the forces/velocities generated, to improve precision, to preserve reachable workspace, or to optimise the geometry of distributed resources.

■ **kinematics**

a kinematic analysis of a mechanical system specifies topology, degrees of freedom (DoFs), motions, and constraints, without specification of applied forces/torques or the mass properties of the bodies. The machine state at some time is the set of all instantaneous positions and instantaneous velocities of all bodies in the system, for both linear (translational) and angular (rotational) DoFs of the bodies. Specification of applied forces/torques and solution of the system's motion as a function of time are given by the system's dynamics.

■ **kinetic coefficient of friction**

the coefficient of friction under conditions of macroscopic relative motion between two bodies.

■ **kip**

a term sometimes used to represent a unit load of 1,000 lb.

■ **kish**

free graphite which separates upon slow cooling of molten hypereutectic iron.

■ **kissing (touching)**

gating with minimum metal left at

casting breakoff point, having a gate just 'kiss' the surface.

■ **knit**

textile process that interlocks, in a specific pattern, loops of yarn by means of needles or wires.

■ **knockout pins (ejector pins)**

small diameter pins affixed to a pattern back-up plate for removing cured mould in the shell-moulding process.

■ **knoop hardness number (hk)**

a number related to the applied load and to the projected area of a rhombic-based diamond indentor, with edge angles of 172 1/2 30' and 130 1/2.

■ **ladle**

metal receptacle frequently lined with refractories used for transporting and pouring molten metal. Types include hand bull, crane, bottom-pour, holding, teapot, shank, lip-pour.

■ **ladle, bottom-pour**

ladle from which metal flows through a nozzle in the bottom.

■ **ladle, bull**

a large ladle for caring molten metal. Frequently used to designate a transfer ladle.

■ **ladle, lip-pour**

ladle in which the metal is poured over a lip.

■ **ladle, teapot**

a ladle in which, by means of an external spout, metal is removed from the bottom rather than the top of the ladle.

■ **lagging**

a light gauge steel covering used over a boiler, usually combined with insulation, to provide a low temperature outer surface.

■ **lamina**

subunit of a laminate consisting of one or more adjacent plies of the same material with identical orientation.

■ **lamina orientation**

see **ply orientation**.

■ **laminar flow**

flow has a smooth appearance and lacks the intense mixing phenomena and eddies of common of turbulent flow.

■ **laminate**

any fibre- or fabric-reinforced composite consisting of laminae with one or more orientations with respect to some reference direction.

■ **laminate coordinate axes**

set of coordinate axes, usually right-handed Cartesian, used as a reference in describing the directional properties and geometrical structure of the laminate. Usually the x-axis and the y-axis lie in the plane of the laminate and the x-axis is the reference axis from which ply angle is measured. The x-axis is often in the principal load direction of the laminate and/or in the direction of the laminate principal axis. (See also principal axis, off-axis laminate, x-axis.)

lance, oxygen

a device, consisting of steel pipe, tubing, oxygen source, and controls which uses the heat of burning steel pipe for melting. Frequently used to open frozen tape or slag holes.

land

gate dimension parallel to the direction of melt flow.

lantern ring

a nylon or metal ring on some packed joint heat exchangers. The lantern ring fits over the outside diameter of the floating tubesheet between the packing rings. When the joint is tightened it holds the packing rings in place. The Lantern Ring also has small holes which act as leak detectors. The leak detectors let the customer know if one of the fluids is leaking around the packing rings. The fluids never mix.

lap joint flange

also called Van Stone. These flanges are used to reduce the amount of an expensive material (S/S) required to make a flange.

A steel ring is used in tandem with the more exotic material. The exotic material will be at the fluid contact surfaces or where the fluid touches the flanges. The steel ring contains the bolt holes. These flanges are also used on stainless steel C-200 type heat exchangers for tubesheets.

lateral expansion

a measured property used in Charpy Impact Testing. Refers to the increase width of the specimen after fracture.

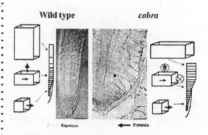

layup

process of placing layers of reinforcing material placed in position in the mould. The reinforcing materials placed in the mould.

layup code

designation system for abbreviating the stacking sequence of laminated composites.

leadthrough programming

a means of teaching a robot by leading it through the operating sequence with a control console or a hand-held control box.

leakage

the amount of fluid passing

through a valve when it is off. It is usually expressed in units of volume/time at a given pressure and temperature.

leakage rate

aRCA standard is 0.01% of Kvs-value (equivalent also to ANSI class IV), increasing by grinding or soft sealing (see also VID 2174, IEC 534 and DIN 3230).

LED

Light Emitting Diode. Often used in calculator displays.

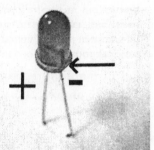

LEFM

abbreviations for Linear Elastic Fracture Mechanics. A method of fracture analysis that can determine the stress required to induce fracture instability in a structure with a crack like flaw of know size and shape.

LERT

a classification system for robots based on the movements Linear, Extensional, Rotation, and Twist.

liberation

see **heat release**.

limit control

a switching device that completes

or breaks an electrical circuit at predetermined pressures or temperatures. Also known as an interlock. See interlock.

linear

a straight line relationship between two variables.

linear characteristics

common design, but especially for the start-up procedures and low flow applications not suitable. Good controllability.

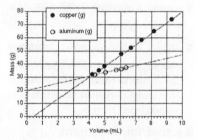

lining

the material used on the furnace side of a furnace wall. It is usually of high grade refractory tile or brick or plastic refractory material.

lining, monolithic

a lining made without the customary layers and joints of a brick wall. Usually made by tamping or casting refractory material into place, drying, and then burning in place on the job.

liquid drop

a small body of liquid held together primarily by surface tension.

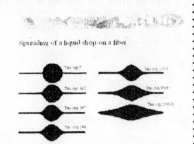

Spreading of a liquid drop on a fiber

■ **liquid holdup**
in-situ flowing volume fraction of liquid.

■ **liquid impingement damage**
see damage.

■ **liquid impingement erosion**
progressive loss of original material from a solid surface due to continued exposure to impacts by liquid drops or jets.

■ **liquid impingement**
impingement by liquid particles.

■ **liquid jet**
a body of liquid projected into motion, usually of approximately cylindrical shape, such as could be produced by discharging the liquid through an orifice. In liquid impingement testing two kinds of liquid jet are used:
1. continuous jet – a continuous flow of liquid in the form of a jet.
2. slug, or jet segment – a body of liquid projected into motion, in the form approximately of a finite cylinder whose length is usually no more than several times its diameter and which moves in a direction approximately parallel to its

length. lubricant, any substance interposed between two surfaces for the purpose of reducing the friction or wear between them.

■ **liquid penetrant testing**
a non-destructive testing method suitable for evaluating the surface integrity of non-magnetic and ferro-magnetic parts.

■ **liquid-crystal polymers (lcp)**
high-performance melt-processible thermoplastics that develop high orientation in the melt and after moulding, resulting in very high tensile strength and high-temperature capability.

■ **list of material resistance**
resistance of material for aggressive and corrosive media on request.

■ **load**
the rate of output required; also the weight carried.

■ **load capacity**
the maximum amount of wait a robot can handle without failure.

■ **load factor**
the ratio of the average load in a given period to the maximum load carried during that period.

■ **local CS**
a local coordinate system (CS) is attached to either a ground or a Body:
grounded CS
Body CS
You define Body CSs when you configure the properties of a

Body. A grounded CS is automatically defined when you represent a ground point by a ground block. A *grounded CS* is always at rest in the World reference frame. The origin of this grounded CS is the same point as the ground point and therefore in general not the same as the World CS origin.

A *Body CS* is fixed rigidly in the body and carried along with that body's motion. To indicate an attached coordinate system, a Body block has a special axis triad CS port in place of the open, round connector port O.

■ **logo**

the sign, mark, or distinguishing letter designating the manufacturer.

■ **look-up table**

in computers, an electronic memory that contains information in table form.

■ **loose moulding**

the moulding process utilising unmounted patterns. Gates and runners are usually cut by hand.

■ **loose piece**

1. core box: part of the core box which remains embedded in the core and is removed after lifting off the core box.
2. Pattern: laterally projecting part of a pattern so attached that it remains in the mould until the body of the pattern is drawn. Back-draft is avoided by this means.
3. Permanent mould: part which remains on the casting and is re-moved after the casting is ejected from the mould.

■ **lost foam process**

casting process in which a foam pattern is removed fro the cavity by the molten metal being poured.

■ **lot**

see **batch**.

■ **low gas pressure control**

a control to stop the burner if gas pressure is too low.

■ **low noise cages**

are often used for noise reduction in steam and gas application.

■ **low oil temperature control**

(Cold Oil Switch), a control to prevent burner operation if the temperature of the oil is too low.

■ **low stress scratching abrasion**

abrasion involving near zero impingement angle for the striking particle, also parallel flow erosion.

■ **low water cutoff**

safety device that shuts off the boiler/burner in the event of low water, preventing pressure vessel failure.

■ **lower heating value (LHV)**

the theoretical heat of combustion of a fuel, when no credit is taken for the heat of condensation of water in the flue gas. It is also called net heating value.

■ **lubricator**

a device used to add lubricants into a fluid power system.

■ **lug**

any projection, like an ear, used for supporting or grasping.

■ **machine allowance**

stock added to the part to permit machining of the part to final dimensions.

■ **machine drawing**

an engineering drawing which depicts the final size and shape of the part for its end use.

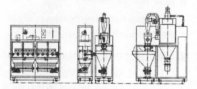

■ **machine language**

the code, in 1's and 0's, of electronic logic that is the direct language of a computer.

■ **machine precision constraint**

a machine precision constraint is a constraint numerically implemented on the constrained degrees of freedom to the precision of your computer processor's arithmetic.
The precision to which the constraint is maintained depends on scale or the physical system of units.

■ **magnetic particle inspection**

a non-destructive method of inspecting the surface integrity of ferromagnetic materials.

■ **magnetostrictive cavitation test device**

a vibratory cavitation test device driven by a magnetostrictive transducer.

■ **make-up**

the water added to boiler feed to compensate for that lost through exhaust, blowdown, leakage, etc.

■ **mandrel**

a form, fixture or male mould used as the base for production of a part in processes such as lay-up or filament winding.

■ **manganese steel (austenitic)**

see **hadfield manganese steel**.

■ **manhole**

the opening in a pressure vessel of sufficient size to permit a man to enter.

■ **manifold**

a pipe or header for collection of a fluid from, or the distribution of a fluid to a number of pipes or tubes.

■ **manipulator**

the mechanical arm mechanism, consisting of a series of links and joints, which accomplishes the motion of an object through space.

■ **manual gas shutoff valve**

a manually operated valve in a gas line for the purpose of completely turning on or shutting off the gas supply.

manual programming

a means of teaching a robot by physically presetting the cams in a rotating stepping drum, setting limit switches on the axis, arranging, wires, or fitting air tubes.

manufactured gas

fuel gas manufactured from coal, oil, etc., as differentiated from natural gas.

maraging steel

a high alloyed steel that is hardened by both martensite transformation and by age hardening.

martempering (interrupted quenching)

a hardening treatment of a steel involving a slow cool through the martensitic transformation range to reduce stresses associated with the quenching of austenite. An important aspect of martempering is that no transformation product other than martensite should form.

martensite

a generic term used for microstructures formed by diffusionless phase transformations. A constituent found in hardened steel; has a needle like microstructure.
See also **Mf and Ms**.

martensitic stainless steels

a corrosion-resistant ferrous alloy with a predominant martensitic phase.

mass

the proportionality between a force on a body and the resulting translational acceleration of that body.

mass concentration

in multi-component or multiphase mixtures, the mass of a specified component or phase per unit mass or unit volume of the total. (See also particle concentration.)
Notes: Since this term has been used both in a non-dimensional sense (mass per unit mass) and in a dimensional sense (mass per unit volume) it is important to make clear in what sense it is used and what units apply in the latter case.

mass effect

the effect that the mass of a component has on the properties of the material from which the part is made. In castings such effects may arise due to the effect of mass on the solidification and on the rate of temperature change heat treatment.

mass produced

made in great quantity or or by methods making each unit the same.

mass velocity

the mass flow rate per unit of flow area through the tubes. Typical units are lb/sec sq ft.

massless connector

a massless connector is equivalent to two joints whose respective axes are spatially separated by a fixed distance. You can specify the gap distance and the axis of separation. The space between the degrees of freedom is filled by a rigid connector of zero mass.
You cannot actuate or sense a

massless connector.

■ mat

an unwoven textile fabric made of fibrous reinforcing material such as chopped filaments (to produce chopped-strand mat) or swirled filaments (to produce continuous-strand mat) with a binder applied to maintain form. Available in blankets of various widths, weights, thicknesses and lengths. May be oriented.

■ matchplate

a plate of metal or other materials on which patterns and gating systems, split along the parting line, are mounted back to back to form an integral piece.

■ material database

the file of the information on each material acceptably tested for use in mouldflow analyses.

■ matrix

material in which reinforcing fibre of a composite is imbedded: polymer, metal or ceramic.

■ matrix content

amount of matrix present in a composite expressed either as a percent by weight or percent by volume. For polymer-matrix composites this is the resin content. (See also **fibre content**.)

■ maximum allowable working pressure

the maximum gauge pressure permissible in a completed boiler. The MAWP of the completed boiler shall be less than or equal to the lowest design pressure determined for any of its parts. This pressure is based upon either proof tests or calculations for every pressure part of the boiler using nominal thickness exclusive of allowances for corrosion and thickness required for loadings other than pressure. It is the basis for the pressure setting of the pressure relieving devices protecting the boiler.

■ maximum continuous load

the maximum load which can be maintained for a specified period.

■ maximum erosion rate

in cavitation and liquid impingement erosion, the maximum instantaneous erosion rate in a test that exhibits such a maximum followed by decreasing erosion rates. (See also **erosion rate-time pattern.**)
Notes Occurrence of such a maximum is typical of many cavitation and liquid impingement tests. In some instances, it occurs as an instantaneous maximum, in others as a steady-state maximum which persists for some time.

■ maximum instantaneous demand

the sudden load demand on a boiler beyond which an unbalanced condition may be established in the boiler's internal flow pattern and/or surface release conditions.

■ maximum operating pressure differential

the maximum difference between the pressure upstream of a valve and the pressure downstream when measured at specific locations.

■ **maximum rate period**

in cavitation and liquid impingement erosion, a stage following the acceleration period, during which the erosion rate remains constant (or nearly mean depth of erosion, in cavitation and impingement erosion, the average thickness of material eroded from a specified surface area, usually calculated by dividing the measured mass loss by the density of the material to obtain the volume loss and dividing that by the area of the specified surface (also known as mean depth of penetration or MDP). Since that might be taken to denote the average value of the depths of individual pits, it is a less preferred term.)

■ **maximum shear stress**

the critical level for the material.

■ **meallographic structure**

the nature, distribution, and amounts of the metallographic constituents in a metal.

■ **mean depth of penetration**

see **mean depth of erosion**.

■ **mechanical**

having to do with machines or tools.

■ **mechanical atomising oil burner**

a burner which uses the pressure of the oil for atomisation.

■ **mechanical draft**

the negative pressure created by mechanical means.

■ **mechanical properties**

properties of a material that reveal its strength and elastic Behaviour.

■ **meld line**

the juncture of two flow fronts moving in the same direction rather than in opposite directions. Meld lines should be positioned in least sensitive areas.

■ **melt**

the molten material which will fill the mould cavity to form the part.

■ **mesh**

the finite elements.

■ **metalloid**

1. an element intermediate between metals and non-metals possessing both metallic and non-metallic properties, as arsenic
2. sometimes applied to elements commonly bonded in small amounts in steel, as carbon, manganese, boron, silicon, sulphur, and phosphorus.

■ **metallstatic pressure**

a compound phase referring to hydrostatic pressure, substituting metal since Hydro connotes water.

■ **metallurgical bond**

the bond between two metals whose interface is free of voids, oxide films, or discontinuities.

■ **metallurgy**

the science and technology of metals, a broad field that includes but is not limited to the study of internal structures and properties of metals and the effects on them of various processing methods.

■ **metal-matrix composites (MMC)**

continuous carbon, silicon carbide, or ceramic fibres embedded in a metallic matrix material.

■ **metalock**

a method of cold repair of castings and forgings.

■ **metals comparator**

an instrument for testing or identifying metallic and non-metallic parts. Parts are placed in an electromagnetic field and a standard parts in a matched electromagnetic field. Distortions of the magnetic fields are compared on an oscilloscope.

■ **metal-to-metal seal**

a seal effected by very smooth finishes on mating metal parts.

■ **metamic**

a metal ceramic high in $Cr-Al_2O_3$.

■ **metastable (unstable)**

a state of pseudo-equilibrium.

■ **Mexico bay sand**

a sand similar to Michigan City dune sand mined at Selkirk Beach, near Mexico NY., on Lake Ontario. It has a silica content of 90% and over.

■ **meyer hardness test**

a test to determine tendency of a metal to harden when deformed plastically. A series of indentations are made in the metal using a fixed-diameter ball and progressively increasing loads.

■ **mf**

the temperature at which martensite formation finishes during cooling.

■ **mica schist**

a type of micaceous refractory rock used for lining cupolas and other melting furnaces.

■ **mica strainer**

a skim core made of thin mineral silicates crystallising in monoclinic form.

■ **Michigan sand**

core sands of dune or lake sand and bank sands found in Michigan.

■ **micro pipes (microshrinkage)**

tiny cavities, a fraction of a millimeter in diameter, with irregular outlines, which occur in castings. Etching shows they occur at intersections of convergent dendritic directions.

■ **microcast process**

a patented method of precision-casting alloys, as Vitallium, Monel, Inconel and the Haynes Stelite alloys.

■ **microcracking**

microscopic cracks formed in composites when thermal stresses locally exceed the strength of the matrix.

■ **microetching**

etching of metal samples for examination under the microscope.

■ **microformer**

a type of extensometer for measuring elongation of test piece in a tensile test.

■ **micrography**

examination by means of a microscope.

■ **microhardness**

the hardness of microconstituents of a material.

■ **microinch**

0.000001 (1/1,000,000th) of an inch. A common unit of measurement in surface measurement research and in standard roughness (surface) unit values of performance of machinery.

■ **microlug**

a test coupon used to give rapid indication of the effectiveness of magnesium treatment of ductile iron.

■ **micron**

one millionth of a meter, or 0.000039 in. or 1/25400 in. The diameter of dust particles is often expressed in microns.

■ **microporosity**

see **microshrinkage**.

■ **microprocessor**

a compact element of a computer central processing unit, con-

structed as a single integrated unit and increasingly used as a control unit for robots.

■ **microradiography**

the process of passing x-rays through a thin section of an alloy in contact with a photographic emulsion, and then magnifying the radiograph 50 to 100 times to observe the distribution of alloying constituents and voids.

■ **microscopic**

minute object or structures which are invisible or not clearly distinguished without the use of a microscope.

■ **microsection**

a metal specimen whose surface has been polished and etched to reveal the microstructure.

■ **microshrinkage**

very finely divided porosity resulting from interdendritic shrinkage resolved only by use of the microscope; may be visible on radiographic films as mottling. Etching shows they occur at intersections of convergent dendritic directions.

■ **microspectroscopy**

a method of identifying metallic constituents using spectrographic arc.

■ **microstructure**

the structure of polished and etched metal and alloy specimens as revealed by the microscope at magnifications over 10 diameters.

■ **micro-tester**

a low load hardness tester, suitable

for both Vickers and Knoop tests, working with loads of between 10 to 3000 grams.

■ **microtone**

an instrument for cutting thin sections of soft specimens.

■ **midplane**

plane that is equidistant from both surfaces of the laminate.

■ **migra iron**

a special pig iron for high quality castings.

■ **micro-tester**

a low load hardness tester, suitable for both Vickers and Knoop tests, working with loads of between 10 to 3000 grams.

■ **mild steel**

plain carbon steel of about 0.25% carbon or less.

■ **mill scale**

iron oxide scale formed on steel during hot working processes, cooled in air.

■ **mill stars**

multi-pointed white iron or hard iron bodies used in a Tumbling Barrel to assist in polishing and cleaning.

■ **milling**

removing metal with a milling cutter.

■ **milliroentgen**

a sub-multiple of the roentgen equal to one-thousandth (1/1000th) of a roentgen.

■ **milliscope**

an instrument which gives an electrical warning when melt reaches a predetermined temperature.

■ **mineral**

natural inorganic substance which is either definite in chemical composition and physical characteristics or any chemical element or compound occurring naturally as a product of inorganic processes.

■ **miniature boiler**

fire pressure vessels which do not exceed the following limits:
16 in. inside diameter of shell; 42 in., overall length to outside of heads at centre; 20 sq ft water heating surface; or 100 psi maximum allowable working pressure.

■ **mischmetal**

an alloy of rare earth metals containing about 50% lanthanum, neodymium, and similar elements.

■ **miscibility**

solubility; ability of two or more liquids to form a homogeneous solution.

■ **misrun**

denotes an irregularity of the casting surface caused by incomplete filling of the mould due to low pouring temperature, gas backpressure from inadequate venting of the mod, and inadequate gating.

■ **mist flow**

characterised by a continuous gas phase with liquid occurring as entrained droplets in th gas stream and as a liquid film wetting the pipe wall.

■ **mitis casting**

casting of very mould steel.

■ **mixed-initiative control**

joint control of a system by humans and machines, usually computer programs that involve automated forms of reasoning. With mixed-initiative control, collections of agents (human and robot), work together, complementing each other's strengths.

■ **MMBtu**

millions of Btus (British Thermal Units).

■ **MMC**

metal-matrix composite.

■ **mock-up**

a full-size model built accurately for study, testing or display.

■ **model**

a proportional representation of an object in any scale.

■ **model number**

a value giving a measure of wear resistance.

■ **modification**

a process in which the eutectic temperature, structure, and composition of aluminium-silicon alloys are apparently altered by the addition of small amounts of a third element, such as sodium. A similar phenomenon can be effected by chill casting.

■ **modulus**

measure of the ratio of applied load (stress) to the resultant deformation of a material. May be represented by a number or in descriptive terms as low, intermediate, high or ultrahigh. (See also **stiffness, Young's modulus**.)

■ **modulus of elasticity**

in tension it is the ration of stress to the corresponding strain within the limit of elasticity (Yield Point) of a material. For carbon and low alloy steels any composition and treatment, the value is approximately 30,000,000 psi.

■ **modulus of resilience**

the amount of strain energy per unit volume required to stress a material from zero to the yield stress limit. The modulus of resilience is proportional to the area under the elastic portion of the stress-strain diagram. Units are Pa or psi.

■ **modulus of rigidity**

in a torsion test the ratio of the unit shear stress to the displacement caused by it per unit length in the elastic range.
See **shear modulus**.

■ **modulus of rupture**

used in both bending and torsion testing. In bending, the modulus of rupture is the bending moment at fracture divided by the section modulus. In torsion, modulus of rupture is the torque at fracture divided by the polar section modulus.

■ **modulus of toughness**

amount of work per unit volume of a material required to carry that material to failure under static loading. Equal to the area under the entire stress-strain curve. Units are Pa or psi.

■ **mogulliser**

equipment for sealing by vacuum impregnation of small pores in castings.

■ **Moh's scale**

a scratch hardness test for determining comparative harness using ten standard minerals, from talc to diamond.

■ **moisture**

water in the liquid or vapour phase.

■ **moisture absorption**

pickup of water vapour from the air by a material. Refers to vapour withdrawn from the air only as distinguished from water absorption, which is weight gain due to the absorption of water by immersion.

■ **moisture content**

the amount of water contained in a substance that can be driven off by heating at 220 - 230°F (104.4 - 110°C).

■ **moisture in steam**

particles of water carried in steam, expressed as the percentage by weight.

■ **moisture loss**

the boiler flue gas loss representing the difference in the heat content of the moisture in the exit gases and that at the temperature of the ambient air.

■ **moisture teller**

a patented apparatus for the rapid determination of moisture content of moulding sand.

■ **molasses water**

a solution of water and molasses sprayed on sand moulds to strengthen mould surface and yield a fine finish layer.

■ **mould**

the blocks containing the cavity, runners and sprue.

■ **mould blower**

moulding equipment for blowing sand mixture onto the pattern with compressed air; allows for faster production than gravity rollover dump.

■ **mould board (follow board)**

the board upon which the pattern is placed to make the mould.

■ **mould cavity**

the space in a mould which is filled with liquid metal to form the casting upon solidification. The channels through which liquid metal enters the mould cavity (sprue, runner, gates) and reservoirs for liquid metal (risers) are not considered part of the mould cavity proper.

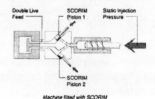

Machine fitted with SCORIM

■ **mould clamp**

devices used to hold or lock cope and drag flask parts together.

■ **mould coating (mould facing, dressing)**

1) coating to prevent surface defects on permanent mould castings and die castings, 2) coating on sand moulds to prevent metal penetration and improve metal finish.

■ **mould cover half (cover die)**

1. the top half of the mould, the cope,
2. in die casting, the front half of the die, which remains stationary as the die is opened.

■ **mould facing**

see **mould coating**.

■ **mould jacket**

a wooden or metal form slipped over a mould to support the side during pouring.

■ **mould shift**

a casting discontinuity resulting from misalignment of the cope and drag halves.

■ **mould temperature**

the temperature at which the mould is maintained. Often the most important benefit of raising mould temperature is that it allows a slower injection rate without the plastic getting too cold.

■ **mouldability**

ability of sand to flow into a flask and around a pattern; measured in the amount of sand falling through an inclined screen or slot.

■ **mouldabilty controller**

a patented device for controlling water additions to sand mix to maintain a consistent mouldability index.

■ **moulding conditions**

the temperature of the mould and melt and the time required to fill the mould.

■ **moulding gravel**

the coarser and more permeable grades of moulding sand generally used in production casting of exceptional size and weight.

■ **moulding material**

a material suitable for making moulds into which molten metal can be cast.

■ **moulding sand mixture**

a sand mixture suitable for making moulds into which molten metal can be cast.

■ **moulding sands**

sands containing over 5% natural clay, usually between 8 and 20%. See also **naturally bonded moulding sand**.

■ **moulding sensitivity**

the variability of the pressure to fill the cavity and temperature of the melt at the part as influenced by changes in injection time and barrel melt temperature.

■ **moulding window**

the range of moulding conditions under which a part can be successfully moulded.

■ **moulding, bench**

making sand moulds by hand tamping loose or production patterns at a bench without assistance of air or hydraulic action.

■ **moulding, floor**

making sand moulds from loose or production patterns of such size that they cannot be satisfactorily handled on a bench or moulding machine, the equipment being located on the floor during the entire operation of making the mould.

■ **moulding, pit**

moulding method in which the drag is made in a pit or hole in the floor.

■ **molecular weight**

weight of the smallest quantity of a substance processing all its normal physical properties.

■ **molecule**

the smallest particle of a substance that can exist in the free state and which has the same composition as any larger mass of the substance.

■ **molybdenum**

a metal used widely in alloying of other metals. It is used as hardening element for steel, and for diecasting dies. Melting point 2620°C (4748°F), atomic number 42.

■ **molybdic oxide**

the oxide of molybdenum; added to the furnace in briquetted form as an important finishing constituent in nitriding steels.

■ **monel**

a high nickel alloy, approximately 67% Ni, 28% Cu, the balance Fe, Mn, Si and other elements. Monel metal is resistant to corrosion and is widely used to resist the action of acids.

■ **monitoring**

1. periodic or continuous determination of the dose rate in an occupied area (area monitoring) or the dose received by a person (personnel monitoring)
2. periodic or continuous determination of the amount of ionising radiation or radioactive contamination present in an occupied region, as a safety measure for purposes of health protection
3. personnel - monitoring any part of any individual, his breath, or excretions, or any part of his clothing.

■ **monitoring area**

routine monitoring of the level of radiation or of radioactive contamination of any particular area, building, room or equipment. Usage in some laboratories or operation distinguishes between routine monitoring and survey activities.

■ **monkey cooler**

in a blast furnace, the smaller of a series of three water coolers protecting the cinder notch. The largest is the cooler, while the in-between cooler is the intermediate cooler.

■ **monocast process**

a patented application of resin-bonded sand to line the flask in the production of centrifugal cast pipe. The resin-bonded layer is thinner than the conventional sand lining.

■ **monofilament**

single continuous filament strong enough to function as a fibre in textile or other operations.

■ **monomer**

a single molecule that reacts with like or unlike molecules to form a polymer.

■ **monotectic**

an isothermal reversible reaction in a binary system, in which a liquid on cooling, decomposes into a solid and a second liquid of different composition.
(Compare with Eutectic.)

■ **monotron**

an instrument for measuring indentation hardness. It is fitted with two dials, one to measure depth of penetration, the other the load.

■ **montmorillonite**

a very plastic clay, more siliceous than kaolinite; the principal constituent of bentonite.

■ **moisture, workable**

that range of moisture content within which sand fills, rams, draws, and dries to a satisfactory mould, and within which the sand does not dry out too fast to mould and patch.

■ **mother metal**

the molten alloy just before final solidification and freezing out of the solid.

■ **motorised variac**

an autotransformer for stepless voltage control in shell moulding.

■ **mottled cast iron**

iron which consists of a mixture of variable proportions of gray iron and white cast iron; such a material has a mottled fracture.

■ **mp**

melting point.

■ **ms**

the temperature at which transformation of austenite to martensite, starts during cooling.

■ **mud**

a term frequently used to designate plastic lining materials.
See also **daubing**.

■ **mud daub**

see **daubing**.

■ **muffle furnace (kiln)**

a furnace in which the heating is indirect; the material to be heated is contained in a refractory container heated from the outside.

■ **muliductor power source**

a device to convert standard 3-phase, 60 cycle current to single-phase, 180-cycle current, so-called medium frequency; produces a strong, controlled stirring action for induction melting.

■ **muller**

a type of foundry sand-mixing machine.

■ **mulling and tempering**

the thorough mixing of sand with

a binder, either natural or added, with lubricant of other fluid, as water.

■ multidirectional flow

flow direction changes during filling resulting in orientation in different directions which can cause flow marks, stresses and warping.

■ multifilament

yarn or tow consisting of many continuous filaments.

■ multifuel burner

a burner by means of which more than one fuel can be burned.

■ multi-objective control

formally, an objective is an artificial potential (with other admissibility properties). A single task may be subject to several simultaneous and varying objectives. Pre-existing control configurations that address narrowly defined objectives (like collision-free motion, force, of kinematic condition) can be composed into robust, multi-objective systems (like walking or grasping).

■ multiple cavity mould

produces more that one identical part with each cycle.

■ multiple mould

a composite mould made up of stacked sections, each of which produces a complete gate of castings, and poured from a central downgate.

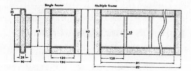

■ multiplexer

the portion of a robot that allows communication with a large number of outside lines, using only a few lines.

■ multiport burner

a burner having a number of nozzles from which fuel and air are discharged.

■ mushet steel

an air hardened steel containing about 2% c, 2% Mn, and 7% W, developed by Scotsman Robert Musket in 1870.

■ mushy stage

the state between sold and liquid in alloys which freeze over a wide range of temperatures.

■ nanotechnology

the scientific field devoted to extremely small human-made devices, both mechanical and electronic. This relatively new branch of science explores the possibilities of building things at the molecular level- atom by atom.

■ natural circulation

the circulation of water in a boiler caused by differences in density.

■ natural draft

system in which the draft required to move combustion air into the heater and flue gas through the heater and out the stack is provided be stack effect alone.

■ natural gas

gaseous fuel occurring in nature.

■ **natural sand**

unconsolidated sand, sand derived from a rock in which grains separate along their natural boundaries. This includes soft sandstone where little pressure is required to separate the individual grains.

■ **naturally balanced runner system**

each succession of runner is identical to the runners in the same succession in all other flows in the mould.

■ **naturally bonded moulding sand**

a sand containing sufficient bonding material as mined to be suitable for moulding purposes. Seldom used today in the metalcasing industry.

■ **nddt**

nil ductility transition temperature, determined in the dropweight test. Refers to the absence of the ductile fracture appearance and any reduction in area due to the brittle Behaviour of the steel.

■ **nde, ndi, ndt**

non-destructive evaluation, non-destructive inspection, non-destructive testing.

■ **near-net shape**

part fabrication resulting in final dimensions that require minimal machining, cutting or other finishing.

■ **neat brick**

brick with faces arranged so one of the flat faces in inclined toward the other, almost eliminating one end face.

■ **neat cement**

portland Cement mixed with water only.

■ **neck down**

a thin core or tile used to restrict the riser neck, making it easier to break or cut off the riser from the casting.
See **core.**

■ **necking**

reducing the cross sectional area of the metal in an area by stretching.

■ **necking down**

reduction in area concentrated at the subsequent location of fracture when a ductile metal is stressed beyond it yield point in tension.

■ **needle point valve**

a type of valve which has a needle point plug and a small seat orifice for metering low flows.

■ **needle valve**

see **needle point valve.**

■ **needles**

elongated acicular crystals, tapering at each end to a fine point, as martensite.

■ **needling agents**

special agents such a boron which markedly increase the hardness of steel.

■ **negative quenching (negative hardening)**

accelerated cooling in water or oil, from a temperature below the critical range.

■ **negative thermoie heat exchange**

in shell moulding, improving the mass-surface ratio by simulating profile geometry of pattern or core cavity on the underside; will boost running temperature of high projections by 25 percent.

■ **nesh**

a British term applied to metal that is weak and ruptures easily under not working conditions.

■ **net positive suction head push**

the difference between total pressure and vapour pressure in a fluid flow, expressed in terms of equivalent height of fluid, or 'head,' by the equation:
$NPSH = (P_o/w) + (V^2/2g).$
(P_v/w)
where:
P_o = static pressure,
P_v = vapour pressure,

V = flow velocity,
w = specific weight of fluid, and.
g = gravitational acceleration.
This quantity is used in pump design as a measure of the tendency for cavitation to occur at the pump inlet. It can be related to the cavitation number.

■ **net positive suction heat (NPSH)**

the liquid pressure that exists at the suction end of a pump. If the NPSH is insufficient, the pump can cavitate.

■ **net shape**

part fabrication resulting in final dimensions that do not require machining or cutting.

■ **network structure**

a structure in which the grains or crystals of one constituent are partly or entirely enveloped in another constituent; an etched section through the crystals resembles a network.

■ **networked sensory and motor services**

a network-distributed system where information sources and effectors are not required to reside on the same platform. Middleware (like Jini, or NDDS) allow client applications to subscribe to information that remote services publish. Sensor and motor services that communicate via a network can be used to assemble short-lived "virtual" robots from spatially distributed resources.

■ **Neumann band**

a mechanical twin in ferrite.

■ **neutral refractories**

a loose term designating refractories which presumably will not react with so-call acid or basic refractories and slags.

■ **neutron**

elementary nuclear particle with a mass (1.00893 mass units) approximately the same as that of a hydrogen atom. It is electrically neutral.

■ **New Jersey sand**

a large number of grades of foundry sands mined in southern New Jersey.

■ **nichrome**

oxidation-resistant alloy 65% Ni, 20% Fe, and 15% Cr.

■ **nickel**

element used for alloying iron and steel as well as non-ferrous metals; melting point 1455°C (2651°F). Nickel is also a base metal for many casting alloys resistant to corrosion and high temperature oxidation.
See monel, nimonic, inconel, Ni-hard.

■ **Ni-hard**

hard white cast iron containing 4% Ni and 2% Cr.

■ **nimonic**

class of nickel-base cast alloy resistant to stress and to oxidation at high temperatures.
See Inconel.

■ **nine-inch equivalent**

standard unit of volume in refractories industries; 9x4-1/2,2-1/2 in brick.

■ **nipple**

a short piece of pipe threaded on both ends.

■ **nital**

a solution of nitric acid in alcohol use as an etching agent in ferrous metallography.

■ **nitriding**

a surface hardening process involving heating in a atmosphere of ammonia or in contact with a nitrogen-bearing material so as to promote the absorption of nitrogen.

■ **nitrogen flush**

bubbling nitrogen gas through a metal melt under vacuum (as with valve bronze) to improve tensile properties and pressure tightness.

■ **nobake binder**

a synthetic liquid resin sand binder that hardens completely at room temperature, generally not requiring baking, used in Cold-Setting process.

■ **noble metals**

metallic elements with surfaces that do not readily oxidise in air; e.g., gold, silver, platinum.

■ **node**

defined by x, y, z coordinates which in turn defines one point of an element (triangle).

■ **nodular fireclay (burley, burley flint)**

rock containing aluminous or ferrogenous nodules, or both, bonded by fireclay.

■ **nodular graphite**

graphite or carbon in modular form, characteristically in malleable and nodular iron.

■ **nodular iron**

iron of a normally gray cast iron type that has been suitably treated with a nodularizing agent so that all or the major portion of its graphitic carbon has a nodular or spherulitic form as cast. Often referred to as ductile iron.

■ **noise radiator**

a device creating noise.

■ **noise spectrum**

the various frequencies making a noise.

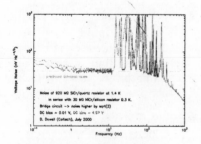

■ **nomex**

trademark of DuPont for moderate-performance meta-aramid material that is often used in paper-form to make honeycomb core.

■ **nomogram (graph)**

a graph that enables one by the aid of a straight-edge to read off the value of a dependent variable when the value of two or more independent variables are given.

■ **nondestructive inspection (NDI)**

determining material or part characteristics without permanently altering the test object. Non-destructive testing (NDT) and nondestructive evaluation (NDE) are broadly considered synonymous with NDI.

■ **nondestructive testing**

testing that does not destroy the object being tested or inspected.

■ **nonferrous**

a negative term, refers to alloy in which the predominate metal or solvent is not iron.

■ **non-ferrous founders society**

see Non-Ferrous Founder's Society for address information.

■ **non-servo control**

the control of a robot through the use of mechanical stops which permit motion between two end points.

■ **nonwoven roving**

reinforcement composed of continuous rovings loosely gathered together. Off-axis laminate Laminate whose principal axis is oriented at an angle theta other than 0° or 90° with respect to a reference direction, usually related to the principal load or stress direction.

■ **normal impact velocity**

see **impact velocity**.

■ **normal segregation**

concentration of alloying constituents that have low melting points in those portions of a casting that solidify last.

■ **normal steel**

steel in which the pearlite is completely laminated.

■ **normalised erosion resistancee**

the volume loss rate of a test material, divided into the volume loss rate of a specified reference material similarly tested and similarly analysed. By 'similarly analysed' is meant that the two erosion rates must be determined for corresponding portions of the erosion rate-time pattern; for instance, the maximum erosion rate or the terminal erosion rate.
Notes: A recommended complete wording has the form, 'The normalised erosion resistance of (test material) relative to (reference material) based on (criterion of data analysis) is (numerical value).'

■ **normalised incubation resistance**

in cavitation and liquid impingement erosion, the incubation period of a test material, divided by the incubation period of a specified reference material similarly tested and similarly Analysed. (See

also **normalised erosion resistance**.)

■ **normalising**

heating a ferrous alloy to a suitable temperature above the transformation temperature Ac3, followed by cooling at a suitable rate, usually in still air to a temperature substantially below the transformation range.

■ **normally closed**

a condition of no flow through a valve or other system when there is no input signal.

■ **normally open**

a valve or other device which allows fluid flow when there is no input signal. An input action must be applied to close the valve.

■ **normally open solenoid valve**

a valve in which the inlet port is open when the solenoid coil is de-energized.

■ **notch bar**

small size ingot with notches to facilitate breakage for remelting.

■ **notched bar**

a test specimen which is notched. Used in impact or fatigue tests.

■ **novalak**

a two-step basic flake resin with no thermosetting properties, applied to sand in shell moulding process as a mould or solution.

■ **NOx**

abbreviation for all of the family of oxides of nitrogen.

■ nozzle

hollow metal hose screwed into the extrusion end of the heating cylinder of an injection machine designed to form a seal under pressure between the cylinder and the mould.

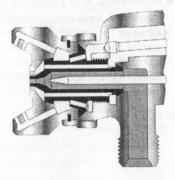

■ nozzle brick

a thick-walled tubular refractory shape set in bottom of a ladle through which steel is teemed.

■ nozzle pocket brick

a refractory shape set in bottom of a ladle containing a recess in which nozzle is set.

■ NTP

normal temperature and pressure reference point; zero centigrade 760 mm mercury pressure.

■ nucleation

1. (homogeneous) the initiation of solid crystals from the liquid stage, or initiation of solid crystals from the liquid stage, or a new phase within a solid without outside interference - rarely occurs
2. (heterogeneous) foreign particles altering the liquid-solid interface energy during phase changes.

■ nucleus

the first structurally determinate particle of a new phase or structure that may be about to form. Applicable in particular to solidification, recrystallisation, and transformations in the solid state.

■ null space

the set of arguments of a linear operator such that the corresponding function value is zero. Redundant systems have a (local) null space that can be used to address a secondary objective, such as kinematic conditioning, without disturbing a primary task.

■ numerical control

a means of providing prerecorded information that gives complete instructions for the operation of a machine.

■ observation doors

viewing ports placed at selected points along the heater walls, to permit viewing of tubes, supports, and burners. It is also called "peep doors".

■ oddsides

semi-permanent moulds of plaster of paris, graphite, or dry sand, tarred and dried and used for repetitive work in the foundry.

■ off iron

pig iron not of the desired composition.

■ off-dimension

a casting defect caused by any incorrect dimension resulting from improper setting of cores, using wrong core, shifts, swells, etc.

■ **off-gauge (off-size)**

core defect caused by improper gaugging of dimensions.

■ **off-grade metal**

metal whose composition does not correspond to the designated or applicable specification.

■ **off-line programming**

a means of programming a robot by developing a set of instructions on an independent computer and then using the software to control the robot at a later date.

■ **oil and gas separator**

a pressure vessel used for separating well fluids produced from oil and gas wells into gaseous and liquid components.

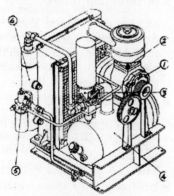

■ **oil and whiting test**

a method of detecting fine cracks by applying a penetrating oil and painting the tested metal surface with a mixture of whiting and a thinner. Oil in the cracks emerges to stain the whiting.

■ **oil burner**

a burner for firing oil.

■ **oil core or mould**

a core or mould in which the sand is bonded by an oil binder.

■ **oil heating and pumping set**

a group of apparatus consisting of a heater for raising the temperature of the oil to produce the desired viscosity, and a pump for delivering the oil at the desired pressure.

■ **oil quenching**

quenching in oil.
See **quenching**.

■ **oil sands**

sand bonded with such oils as linseed and the synthetics.

■ **oil shot**

in die casting, a sponge like whirl on the surface of casting resulting from an excess of oil applied to the sprue hole before the shot was made.

■ **oil-oxygen binder (cold-setting, air-setting binders)**

a synthetic auto-oxidising liquid, oil-based binder that partially hardens at room temperature, using an oxygen releasing agent. Baking is needed to complete the hardening.

■ **olive**

($Mg_2Fe_2SiO_4$) A naturally occurring mineral composed of fosterite and fayalite, crushed and used as a moulding sand. Usually the sand of choice in manganese steel casting due to its basicity.

■ one-off

fabrication process in which a single part is fabricated.

■ one-part resin system

resin system (often used in resin transfer moulding) in which the neat resin and catalyst are mixed together by the materials supplier as part of the resin production operation.

■ one-piece pattern

solid pattern, not necessarily made from one piece of material. May have one or more loose pieces.

■ one-screen

a distribution of a clean sand or a sand with two maximum screens separated by a minimum screen. These high-expansion problem sands are also referred to as camel back distributions.

■ on-line programming

a means of programming a robot on a computer that directly controls the robot. The programming is performed in real time.

■ on-off control

a system of control in which the final control element has only two positions from which to choose. It is also known as two-position control.

■ open face mould

see **open sand casting**.

■ open flame furnace

as opposed to the crucible furnace; in the open-flame furnace the metal charge is confined in the refractory lining, with the flame and products of combustion coming in direct contact with the metal.

■ open grain structure

a defect wherein a casting, when machined or fractured, appears to be coarse grained and porous; usually due to a shrink area.

■ open riser

see **riser open**.

■ open sand casting

a casting produced in an open mould; poured in the drag, with no cope or other top covering.

■ open system

you can disconnect an *open system* into two separate systems by cutting no more than one joint. Such systems can be divided into two types:
An *open chain* is a series of bodies connected by joints and topologically equivalent to a line.
An *open tree* is a series of bodies connected by joints in which at least one body has more than two joints connected to it. Bodies with more than two connected joints define *branch points* in the tree. A tree can be disconnected into multiple chains by cutting the branch points.
The end body of a chain is a body with only one connected joint.

■ open hearth furnace

a furnace for melting metal, in which the bath is heated by the combustion of hot gases over the surface of the metal and by radiation from the roof.

■ **operating control**

a control to start and stop the burner must be in addition to the high limit control.

■ **operating pressure**

the pressure at which a boiler is operated.

■ **operating temperature**

the nominal or average temperature of a fluid in a system.

■ **optical pyrometer**

a temperature measuring device through which the observer sights the heated object and compares its incandescence with that of an electrically heated filament whose brightness can be regulated; or the intensity of the light admitted from the object may be varied through filters and compared with a constant light source.

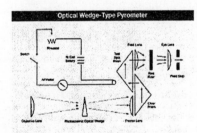

■ **optimum moisture**

that moisture content which results in developing the maximum of any property of a sand mixture.

■ **orange peel**

a pebble-grained surface that develops in the mechanical forming of sheet metals with coarse grains.

■ **orange peel bucket**

a bottom-drop bucket used for charging cupolas; the drop-bottom is divided into a number of sections that appear to peel back as the bucket opens.

■ **ore**

a mineral from which a metallic element may be extracted profitably.

■ **organic matter**

compounds containing carbon often derived from living organisms.

■ **orientation**

the arrangement of the molecules of the melt. If the molecules are orientated, they are aligned with each other; if non-orientated they are not in alignment. In general, orientated material shrinks more than non-orientated material.

■ **orifice plate**

in a cupola a device used to measure the volume of air delivered to the windbox.

■ **orifice**

1. the opening from the whirling chamber of a mechanical atomiser or the mixing chamber of a steam atomiser through which the liquid fuel is discharged. 2. A calibrated opening in a plate, inserted in a gas stream to measure velocity of flow.

■ **ORSAT**

a gas-analysis apparatus in which certain gaseous constituents are measured by absorption in separate chemical solution.

■ **oscillating trough cooler**

a steel trough conveyor within a plenum where reclaimed sand is cooled prior to reuse.

■ **OSHA**

Occupational Safety and Health Administration.

■ **osmondite**

an obsolete term once used to designate a ferrous microstructure not so well defined as Troosite.

■ **Ottowa sand**

a sand originating near Ottawa Ill., also know as St. Peter sandstone.

■ **out time**

period of time in which a prepreg remains handleable with properties intact outside a specified storage environment (such as a freezer, in the case of thermoset prepregs).

■ **outer tube limit**

the O.T.L. is the diameter created by encircling the outer most tubes in a tube layout. The design O.T.L. is used by engineers to calculate clearances between bundle parts. The actual O.T.L. is usually a few thousandths less than the design O.T.L.

■ **outgassing**

release of solvents and moisture from composite parts under the hard vacuum of space.

■ **outlet header**

the collection manifold by which the exiting process fluid is collected.

■ **out-of-round**

failure to remain round.

■ **oven, drying**

a furnace or oven for drying moulds or cores.

■ **ovens**

see **continuous annealing furnace**.

■ **overaging**

aging a precipitation-hardening alloy under conditions of time and temperature greater than those required to obtain maximum strength or hardness.

■ **overfiring**

heating refractories to a temperature sufficient to cause pronounced vitrification, deformation, or bloating.

■ **overflows (overflow wells)**

separated cavities cut into the face of die casting dies adjacent to the main cavity and connected to it by a channel, ensuring filling of cavity.

■ **overhand**

extension of the end surface of the cope half of a core print beyond that of the drag to provide clearance for closing of the mould.

■ **overheated**

a term applied when, after exposure to an excessively high temperature, a metal develops an undesirable coarse grain structure, but is not necessarily damaged permanently. Unlike burned structure, the structure produced by overheating can be corrected by suitable heat treatment, by mechanical work, or by a combination of the two.

■ **overpack**

melt will fill the easiest flow path first and will continue to pack this area while material reaches the other areas. This is a cause of warping created by unbalanced flow.

■ **overpressure**

minimum operating pressure of a hot water boiler sufficient to prevent the water from steaming.

■ **overshoot**

the exceeding or surpassing of a target value as operating conditions change.

■ **overstressing**

permanently deforming a metal by subjecting it to stresses that exceed the elastic limit.

■ **Owen jet dust counter**

an instrument similar to the konimeter, using the humidification factor.

■ **oxidation**

any reaction of an element with oxygen. In a narrow sense, oxidation means the taking on of oxygen by an element or compound, and on the basis of the electron theory it is a process in which an element loses electrons.

■ **oxidation losses**

reduction in amount of metal or alloy through oxidation. Such losses usually are the largest factor in melting loss.

■ **oxide**

a compound of oxygen with another element.

■ **oxidising atmosphere**

an atmosphere resulting from the combustion of fuels in an atmosphere where excess oxygen is present, and with no unburned fuel lost in the products of combustion.

■ **oxygen attack**

corrosion or pitting in a boiler caused by oxygen.

■ **oxygen bomb calorimeter**

an instrument to measure the heats of combustion of solid and liquid fuels.

■ **oxygen impingement process**

pure oxygen is blown down on the bath to refine pig iron.

■ **packaged boiler**

a boiler supplied with all of its components burner, controls and auxiliary equipment, designed as a single engineered package, and ready for on-site installation.

■ **packaged steam generator**

see **packaged boiler.**

■ **packed end**

the end of a heat exchanger which contains the packed joint. This packed joint contains the packing rings. It is also called the floating end of the unit, where the floating tubesheet is located.

■ **packing**

a device used to seal a valve or

other components. It consists of a deformable material or deformable mating element.

■ **packing follower**

a ring shaped device that is installed on top of the packing to hold it in place. It may also be used to adjust the pressure on the packing.

■ **packing or packing material**

sand, gravel, mill scale or similar materials used to support castings packed in annealing pots, to prevent possible warpage under high temperatures.

■ **packing ring**

a fairly soft non-metallic ring which is used to seal the floating tubesheet or packed end of the heat exchanger. The packing ring slips over the floating tubesheet on either side of the lantern ring. It also fits into a groove in the shell and bonnet flange, or is held in place by retaining ring assembly.

■ **padding**

the process of adding metal to a cross section of a casting wall, usually extending from a riser, to ensure adequate feed to a localised area where a shrink would occur if the added metal were not present.

■ **painting system**

this is a surface coating with a mixture of Polyurethane consequently no colour which is very solid.

■ **pallet**

a flat bed, usually made from wood, used for transportation and storage of goods.

■ **palletising**

the process of placing parts in different positions on a pallet.

■ **PAN**

same as polyacrylonitrile.

■ **panel spalling test**

a test using a panel of the refractory being tested to provide a reference to spalling Behaviour.

■ **panoramic analyser**

an instrument for Analysing sounds and displaying the results either on an oscilloscope or a graph.

■ **papping plate**

a metal plate attached to a pattern to prevent injury to the pattern and assist in loosening it from the sand.

■ **parameter**

a set of constant factors applying to a particular situation.

■ **parkerising**

a proprietary method of producing a protective phosphate coating on ferrous metals. Parker A treatment involves immersing in a bath of acid manganese phosphate. The Parker D is a modification using acid zinc phosphate with a nitrate iron as accelerator.

■ **parlanti casting process**

a proprietary permanent mould process using dies of aluminium with a controlled rate of heat transfer.

Parsons Duncan process

a method of casting steel ingots wherein the top layer of the mould is heated and the last to solidify.

part

the payload formed in the cavity.

part consolidation

process of composites fabrication in which multiple discrete parts are designed and fabricated together into a single part, thus reducing the number of fabricated parts and the need to join those parts together.

part quality

minimal residual stress level, avoiding both warpage and sink marks.

parted pattern

a pattern made in two or more parts.

partially graphitised cast iron

a blackheart malleable casting only partly graphitised in annealing, giving a mixture of black and white. Sometimes termed salt and pepper fracture.

partially-balanced runner system

composed of both naturally and artificially balanced runners.

particle concentration

a measure of the liquid or solid particle content in a mixture of particles and fluid. The following more specific terms are in use:
1. rain density – the mass of liquid per unit volume of mixture in an actual or simulated rainfield.
2. solids loading ratio – the mass of solid particles per unit volume of mixture in a solid impingement environment.
3. volume concentratio the volume of the liquid or solid particles per unit volume of mixture.
4. quality-the mass of vapour phase per unit mass of a liquid-vapour two-phase single-component fluid.
5. mass concentration.

particle size

a measure of dust size, expressed in microns or per cent passing through a standard mesh screen.

particulate matter

in air pollution control, solid or liquid particles, except water, visible with or without a microscope, that make up the obvious portion smoke.

parting agent

see **release agent**.

parting line

a line on a pattern or casting corresponding to the separation between the cope and drag portions of a sand mould.

parting line

mark on the part indicating where the two halves of the mould met in closing.

pass

a coil, which carries the process fluid from heater inlet and outlet. One can transport the total process fluid through the heater using parallel passes.

■ **pass lane**

a lane in a tube layout where there are no tubes. The pass lane is the surface on the tubesheets where the pass ribs mate.

■ **pass rib**

a separator plate inside a bonnet or channel. This rib mates with the pass lane surface. It is used to create multi-pass heat exchangers. By arranging the ribs, a designer can control the flow of the tubeside medium.

■ **passivator**

an inhibitor which changes the potential of a metal to a more cathodic value.

■ **passivity**

the property of some metals to become abnormally inactive towards certain reagents.

■ **patching**

repair of a furnace lining; repair of a mould core.

■ **pattern**

a form of wood, plastic, metal, or other material around which moulding material is placed to make a mould.

■ **pattern draft**

the taper on vertical elements in a pattern which allows easy separation of pattern from compacted sand mixture.

■ **pattern layout**

full-sized drawing of a pattern showing its arrangement and struc-

ture features.

■ **patternmaker**

a craftsman engauged in production of foundry patterns from wood, plastic, or metals, such as aluminium, brass, etc.

■ **payload**

the maximum amount that can be handled by a robot during normal operation.

■ **PCE**

pyrometric cone equivalent.

■ **pearlite**

a lamella aggregate of ferrite and carbide, the structure of pearlite can appear fine or coarse depending on processing.

■ **peel ply**

layer of material applied to a prepreg layup surface that is removed from the cured laminate prior to bonding operations, leaving a clean, resin-rich surface ready for bonding.

■ **peel strength**

strength of an adhesive bond obtained by stress that is applied in a 'peeling' mode.

■ **peen**

peening action obtained by impact of metal shot, often used to improve fatigue properties by putting the surface in compression.

■ **pencil core**

a core projecting to the centre of a blind riser allowing atmospheric pressure to force out feed metal.

■ **penetrameter**

a strip of metal with stepped thickness variation and with holes at varying depths; used in radiography to indicate the sensitivity of the radiograph.

■ **penetration, metal**

condition where molten metal has penetrated into the sand, resulting in a mixture of metal and sand adhering to the casting.

■ **perfect combustion**

the complete oxidation of all the combustible constituents of a fuel, utilising all the oxygen supplied.

■ **perforated plug**

control plug with seat guiding results in noise reduction and is cavitation-resistant. Also multi-step designs are available, good adaptation to control purposes possible.

■ **periclase**

natural magnesia in nodular form, formed by heating.

■ **perlite**

a highly siliceous volcanic rock which can be expended by heat-

ing into a porous mass of particles. Perlite can be used as an insulation in foundry sand mixtures. Not to be confused with Pearlite.

■ **permanent mould**

a metal mould of two or more parts; not an ingot mould. It is used repeatedly for the production of many casting of the same form.

■ **petroleum**

naturally occurring mineral oil consisting predominately of hydrocarbons.

■ **pH**

the hydrogen ion concentration of a water to denote Acidity or Alkalinity. A pH of 7 is neutral. A pH above 7 denotes alkalinity while one below 7 denotes acidity. This pH number is the negative exponent of 10 representing hydrogen ion concentration in grams per liter. For instance a pH of 7 represent 10^{-7} grams per liter.

■ **phase diagram**

a graphic representation of the equilibrium temperature and composition limits of phase fields reactions in an alloy system. In a binary system, temperature is usually the ordinate and composition the abscissa. Ternary and more complex systems require several two-dimensional diagrams to show the temperature – composition variables completely. In alloy systems, pressure is usually considered constant, although it may be treated as an additional variable.

Phase Diagram for a Multicomponent System in Water

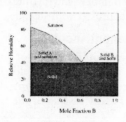

phenolic resin

thermosetting resin produced by a condensation reaction of an aromatic alcohol with an aldehyde (usually phenol with formaldehyde).

phenolic resin (one-step)

a resin made by the Polymerisation of a phenol with an aldehyde; used a binder for cores and sand moulds.
See **urea-form-aldehyde resin.**

photomicrograph

a photograph of the grain structure of a metal as observed when optically magnified more than 10 diameters. The term micrograph may be used.

physical metallurgy

the science concerned with the physical and mechanical characteristics of metals and alloys.

physical tree

you obtain the physical tree representation of a machine topology from the full machine topology by removing actuators and sensors and cutting each closed loop once. The physical tree retains bodies, joints, constraints, and drivers.

pick and place robot

a simple category of robot used to pick parts and place them down somewhere else.

picral

an etchant for ferrous alloys; 4% picric acid in alcohol.

pig iron, basic

a grade of iron made from the basic open-hearth process of steelmaking; P, 0.40% max. for Northern iron, 0.70 to 0.90% for Southern iron; S 0.05% max. and Si, 1.50%.

pig iron

pig iron ores very low in phosphorus; copper-free and containing appreciable amounts of titanium.

pilot

a flame which is utilised to ignite the fuel at the main burner or burners.

pilot casting

casting produced prior to the production run to verify correctness of procedures, materials, and process to be used in production.

pilot plant

a full-scale working factory used as a model of manufacturing techniques for other plants.

pilot valve

a device acting between the source pressure and the actuator that directs (controls) flow.

pin holes

small holes that penetrate the surface of a cured part.

■ **pipe**

a cavity formed by shrinkage of the metal during solidification, usually occurring in a riser having feeder metal for the casting.

■ **pitch**

residual petroleum product used as a precursor in the manufacture of certain carbon fibres.

■ **pitot tube**

an instrument which will register total pressure and static pressure in a gas stream, used to determine its velocity.

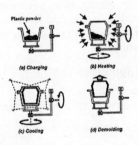

(a) Charging   (b) Heating

(c) Cooling   (d) Demolding

■ **pitting**

a form of wear characterised by the presence of surface cavities, the formation of which is attributed to processes such as fatigue, local adhesion, cavitation or corrosion.

■ **pizza effect**

should be better called the 'hamburger' effect which describes the squeezing out of the actuator diaphragm between both the shells of the actuator body. This problem has been solved by the chambering of the ARCA multi-spring actuator.

■ **plane strain**

a stress condition in linear elastic fracture mechanics (See LEFM) in which there is zero strain in a direction normal to both the axis of applied tensile stress and the direction of crack growth. Under plane strain conditions, the plane of fracture instability is normal to the axis of the principal tensile stress.

■ **plasma refining**

process used to reduce sulphur and oxygen to very low levels.

■ **plaster of paris**

a semi-hydrated form of calcium sulphate made by sintering gypsum to
120 - 130 °C (248 − 266 °F).

■ **plastic deformation**

permanent distortion of a material under the action of applied pressure.

■ **plates, core drying**

flat plates of metal on which cores are placed for baking.

■ **plied yarn**

two or more yarns collected together with or without twist.

■ **plots**

graphical representations of analysis results.

■ **plowing**

in tribology the formation of grooves by plastic deformation of the softer of two surfaces in relative motion.

■ **plug flow**

large gas bubbles flow along the top of the pipe, which is otherwise filled with liquid.

■ **ply**

constituent single layer used in fabricating or occurring within a composite structure. Also, the number of single yarns twisted together to form a plied yarn.

■ **ply orientation**

acute angle (theta).

■ **ply schedule**

layup of individual plies or layers to form a laminate. Plies may be arranged in alternating fibre orientation to produce multidirectional strength in a part.

■ **PMMA**

polymethymethacralate - Foam used in the lost foam process, does release as much carbon as polystyrene.

■ **pneumatic**

of air.

■ **pohland method**

a technique for the ultrasonic testing of steel in which a visible image of the defects present in the steel can be shown on a screen.

■ **t-to-point motion**

'pe of robot motion in which limited number of points along a path of motion is specified by the controller, and the robot moves from point to point rather than in a continues, smooth path.

■ **polar winding**

filament winding in which the filament path passes tangent to the polar opening at one end of the chamber and tangent to the opposite side of the polar opening at the other end of the chamber.

■ **polyacrylonitrile (PAN)**

base material in the manufacture of some carbon fibres.

■ **polyimide**

highly heat-resistant polymer resin.

■ **polymer**

large organic molecule formed by combining many smaller molecules (monomers) in a regular pattern.

■ **polymerisation**

chemical reaction that links monomers to form polymers.

■ **polystyrene**

a polymer of styrene used in making moulding products. In particular, used in the lost foam process.

■ **porosity**

presence of visible voids within a solid material into which either air or liquids may pass.

■ **port**

an opening through which fluid passes.

■ **positioner**

a control accessory that accepts a varying input signal and direct air to the actuator to position the valve for flow control.

■ **post purge**

a method of scavenging the furnace and boiler passes to remove all combustible gases after flame failure controls have sensed pilot and main burner shutdown and safety shut-off valves are closed.

■ **postcure**

additional exposure to elevated temperature, often occurring without tooling or pressure, that improves mechanical properties.

■ **postheating**

a process used immediately after welding whereby heat is applied to the weld zone either for tempering or for providing a controlled rate of cooling, in order to avoid a hard or brittle structure.

■ **pot life**

length of time in which a catalysed thermosetting resin retains sufficiently low viscosity for processing.

■ **potential field**

a twice differentiable function with the sum of partial derivatives equal to zero over some input space. Intuitively, a potential is a measurable quantity that has no net change in value along any path that starts and ends at the same point. Potential fields are useful, for instance, when designing stable controllers that converge to a minimum value of some quantity.

■ **pouring**

transfer of molten metal from furnace to ladle, ladle to ladle, or ladle into moulds.

■ **pouring cup**

the flared section of the top of the downsprue. It can be shaped by hand in the cope, or be a shaped part of the pattern used to form the downsprue; or may be baked core cup placed on the top of the cope over the downsprue.

■ **powder cutting**

introducing iron powder in an oxygen stream to hasten oxygen torch cutting by the combination of fluxing and oxidation. Generally used for cutting stainless steel.

■ **ppm**

abbreviation for parts per million. Used in chemical determinations as one part per million parts by weight.

■ **precipitate**

to separate materials from a solution by the formation of insoluble matter by chemical reaction. The material which is removed.

■ **precipitation**

the removal of solid or liquid particles from a fluid.

■ **precipitation hardening**

a process of hardening an alloy in which a constituent precipitates from a supersaturated solid solution.

■ **precipition heat treatment**

any of the various aging treatments conducted at elevated temperatures to improve certain mechanical properties through precipitation from solid solution.

■ **precure**

full or partial setting of a resin or adhesive before the clamping operation is complete or before pressure is applied.

■ **precursor**

material from which carbon fibre is made by pyrolysis. Common precursors are polyacrylonitrile (PAN), rayon and pitch.

■ **preform**

pre-shaped fibrous reinforcement, normally without matrix, but often containing a binder to facilitate manufacture; formed by distribution of fibres to the approximate contour and thickness of the finished part, typically on a mandrel or mock-up.

■ **preheated air**

air at a temperature exceeding that of the ambient air.

■ **preheating**

a general term for heating material, as a die in die casting, as a preliminary to operation, to reduce thermal shock and prevent adherence of molten metal.

■ **prepreg**

admixture of fibrous reinforce-
ment and polymeric matrix used to fabricate composite materials in a form that can be stored for later use. It may be sheet, tape, tow or fabric. For thermosetting matrices the resin is usually partially cured or otherwise brought to a controlled viscosity, called B-stage. Additives such as catalysts, inhibitors and flame retardants can be added to obtain specific end-use properties and improve processing, storage and handling characteristics.

■ **press loading**

the placing of material in a stamping or other forming machine.

■ **pressure**

force per unit of area.

■ **pressure balancing**

diaphragm actuators/spindles are limited with regard to the available/permissible control force. Therefore the same pressure adapted to the upper and lower side of the plug by corresponding technical measures.

■ **pressure die casting**

a British term.

■ **pressure differential**

the difference in pressure between any two points in a fluid system. It is also called pressure drop.

■ **pressure drop**

the amount of pressure required to fill that section. Adding up the pressure drops over every section in a flow path totals the pressure required to fill the mould.

■ **pressure regulator**

a valve used to automatically reduce and maintain pressure below that of a source.

■ **pressure switch**

a switch that is operated by a change in the applied pressure.

■ **pressure vessel**

a closed vessel or container designed to confine a fluid at a pressure above atmospheric.

■ **pressure, vapour**

the pressure, at a given temperature, in which the liquid and gaseous phases coexist in equilibrium.

■ **pressure-tight**

a term describing a casting free from porosity of the type that would permit leaking.

■ **primary air**

air introduced with the fuel at the burner.

■ **primary choke (choke)**

that part of the gating system which most restricts or regulates the flow of metal into the mould cavity.

■ **primary crystals**

the first dendritic crystal that form in an alloy during cooling below the liquidus temperature.

■ **primary structure**

an aerospace critical load-bearing structure; if damaged the air- or spacecraft cannot fly.

■ **prime contractors**

referred to as 'primes'; companies that are awarded government contracts and usually work with subcontractors (or "subs") who provide individual and specific components or systems relevant to the contract. Primes often team on contracts, sharing portions of the contract funding.

■ **priming**

the discharge of steam containing excessive quantities of water in suspension from a boiler, due to violent ebullition.

■ **primitive joint**

a primitive joint expresses one degree of freedom (DoF) or coordinate of motion, if this DoF is a translation along one direction (prismatic joint) or a rotation about one fixed axis (revolute joint).

■ **principal axes**

the inertia tensor of a body is real and symmetric and therefore can be diagonalised, with three real eigenvalues and three orthogonal eigenvectors. The principal axes of a body are these eigenvectors.

■ **principal axis**

laminate coordinate axis that coincides with the direction of maximum in plane Young's modulus.

Within a ply, for a balanced weave fabric either warp or fill direction may be chosen.

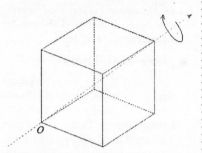

principal inertial moments

the inertia tensor of a body is real, symmetric, and diagonalisable, with three real eigenvalues and three orthogonal eigenvectors. The principal inertial moments or principal moments of inertia of a body are these eigenvalues, the diagonal values when the tensor is diagonalised.

The principal moments of a real body satisfy the triangle inequalities: the sum of any two moments is greater than or equal to the third moment. If two of the three principal moments are equal, the body has some symmetry and is dynamically equivalent to a symmetric top. If all three principal moments are equal, the body is dynamically equivalent to a sphere.

process capability

the amount of variation in the output of a controlled manufacturing process, the range defined by plus or minus three standard deviations.

process steam

steam used for industrial purposes other than for producing power.

product analysis

in castings, the analysis of the actual part as opposed to the analysis of the steel from which the casting was poured.

production welding

any welding carried out during manufacturing before final delivery to the purchaser. This includes joint welding of casting and finishing welding.

products of combustion

the gases, vapours, and solids resulting form the combustion of fuel.

proeutectoid

the constituent that separates out of a solid solution before the formation of eutectoid.

profile tolerances

a system of locating and tolerancing developed to control the orientation of rough parts in machine fixtures. From locating points on the casting a 'perfect profile' is established for all surfaces and features. A tolerance envelope surrounding that profile defines the limitations of an acceptable part.

programmable

a feature of a robot that allows it to be instructed to perform a sequence of steps, and then to perform this sequence in a repetitive manner. It can then be reprogrammed to perform a different sequence of steps, if desired.

■ **programming language**

any of the computer instruction codes that simplifies programming for people.

■ **proportional**

a relationship of one variable to another for which there is a constant ratio.

■ **protection tube**

a metal, graphite, or ceramic tube which shrouds and protects the wires of a thermoelectric pyrometer.

■ **protector rod**

also called a zinc. A sacrificial anode usually placed in the tubeside of a heat exchanger. The zinc protects the tubes, tubesheets and bonnets against corrosion. When water is flowing through the tubeside the zinc is consumed instead of the other heat exchanger parts.

■ **prototype**

process of creating a test part not intended for commercial release that establishes design, material and fabrication parameters for a new product. May entail multiple iterations to arrive at final/commercial part design.

Prototype of TAMA300 suspension

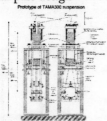

■ **proximity switch**

an electrical device that signals when an object is close to it.

■ **psi**

the abbreviation for pounds per square inch, the unit of pressure in the British Engineering System.

■ **puckers**

local areas on prepreg where material has blistered and pulled away from the separator film or release paper.

■ **pugnill**

a mill for mixing foundry sands and sand mixtures consisting essential of a shaft fitted with plows or paddle wheel which revolve in a tub or vat.

■ **pulsation**

rapid fluctuations in pressure.

■ **pulsed cavitation test**

a test using a vibratory cavitation device in which the cavitation is generated intermittently, with alternating vibratory periods and quiescent periods of controlled relative duration.
Notes such tests are longer than the other vibratory tests and thus approach more closely the time scale of real cavitation erosion. Such tests are useful in investigating chemical effects in cavitation erosion, because the cavitation pulses can remove protective surface films and expose the surface to chemical attack during the quiescent periods.

■ **pultrusion**

continuous process for manufacturing composites in rods, tubes and structural shapes having constant cross sections. After the reinforcement is passed through the resin-impregnation bath, it is drawn through a shaping die to form the desired cross section; curing takes place before the laminate can depart from that cross section.

■ **punchout machines**

a machine used to force the entire sand and casting contents from the moulding box in one motion, without the use of vibration.

■ **puncture**

break in composite skin in sandwich structure that may or may not go through to the core material or completely through the part.

■ **purge**

to introduce air into the furnace and the boiler flue passages in such volume and manner as to completely replace the air or gas-air mixture contained therein.

■ **purging**

elimination of air and other undesirable gases from furnaces or heating boxes.

■ **pv product**

in tribology, the product of the nominal contact pressure on a load-bearing surface and the relative surface velocity between the load-bearing material and its counterface.
Notes Several units have been used for reporting the PV product $(F L^{-2} (L T^{-1}))$ Historically, these have included psi-ft/min and MPa-m/s.

■ **pyrometallurgy**

chemical metallurgical process dependent upon heat.

■ **pyrometric cone**

a slender trihedral pyramid made of a mixture of minerals similar in composition to that of a clay or other refractory being tested. Each cone is assigned a number indicating its fusion temperature.

■ **pyrometric cone equivalent**

an index of refractoriness obtained by heating on a time-temperature schedule a cone of the sample material and a series of standardised pyrometric cones of increasing refractoriness.

■ **pyrometry**

a method of measuring temperature with any type of temperature indicating instruments.

■ **qenching**

rapid cooling of hardening; normally achieved by immersion of the object to be hardened in water, oil, or solutions of salt or organic compounds in water.

■ **quad layout**

a quadrant type tube layout. Four separate quarters of a tube layout with pass lanes between them. The type of tube layout used on all BCF's except the 8" size.

■ **quadraxial fabric**

fabric with four non-interwoven layers.
+45°, -45°, 0° and 90°, which are bonded together, usually by through-the-thickness stitching, to form a single sheet of fabric. (See also **biannual fabric, triaxial fabric**.)

■ **quality circles**

a committee that reviews the quality of a product and makes recommendations for its improvement.

■ **quality**

see **particle concentration**.

■ **quartz**

a form of silica occurring in hexagonal crystals which are commonly colourless and transparent, but sometimes also yellow, brown, purple, green, etc. It is the most common of all solid minerals. See also **silica**.

■ **quartzite**

a compact granular rock composed of quartz. It is a metamorphosed sandstone, and siliceous cement is often so blended with the quartz grains as to give the rock a nearly homogeneous texture. Primary materiel in silica brick.

■ **quasi-isotropic laminate**

a laminate approximating isotropy by orientation of plies in several or more directions.

■ **quaternion**

a quaternion represents a three-dimensional spherical rotation as a four-component row vector of unit length:
$$q = [n_x^* \sin(è/2) \quad n_y^* \sin(è/2) \quad n_z^* \sin(è/2) \quad \cos(è/2)],$$
with $q^*q = 1$. The vector n = (n_x, n_y, n_z) is a three-component vector of unit length: $n^*n = 1$. The unit vector n specifies the axis of rotation. The rotation angle about that axis is è and follows the right-hand rule.
The axis-angle representation of the rotation is just [n è].

■ **quench crack**

a crack resulting from thermal stress induced during rapid cooling or quenching, or from stresses induced by delayed transformations some time after the article has been fully quenched.

■ **quench severity**

the quench severity is characterised by the H value and relates to the rate of temperature change during quenching.

■ **r/w memory**

read and write memory. The memory portion of a computer used by the operator to store programs.

■ **racetrack effect**

thicker area in flow cross section speeds up the flow.

■ **radiant heat**

heat communicated by radiation and transmitted by electromagnetic waves.

■ **radiant section**

the portion of the heater in which heat is transferred to the tubes primarily by radiation from the flame and high-temperature flue gas, and hot refractory.

■ **radiation area**

any part of an installation accessible to employees in which there exists a radiation level of 7.5 millirem in any one hour over 150 millirem in any seven consecutive days.

■ **radiation hazard**

any situation where persons might be exposed to radiation in excess of the maximum permissible dose.

■ **radiation, direct**

all radiation coming from within an x-ray tube and tube housing except the useful beam.

■ **radioactive isotopes**

varieties of an element possessing the same chemical characteristics but emitting detectable radiation's by means of which they can be identified and traced.

■ **radioactive material**

any compound or element which may emit any or all of the following: alpha and beta particles, electrons, photons neutrons and gamma and all other emissions which produce ionisation directly or indirectly.

■ **radium**

a radioactive element which the chemical symbol Ra; radium and its salts are used in gamma-ray radiography because of their radioactivity. Melting point is 700°C (1292°F).

■ **rain density**

see **particle concentration**.

■ **ram**

Random Access Memory. The computer selects the location in which a particular byte is to be stored.

■ **ramming**

packing sand in a mould by raising and dropping the sand, pattern, flask on a table. Jolt squeezers, jarring machines, and jolt rammers are machines using this principle.

■ **ramping**

gradual programmed increase/decrease in temperature or pressure to control cure or cooling of composite parts.

■ **range**

the difference between the highest and lowest values of a measurable attribute of the output of a process.

■ **rangeability**

the ratio of maximum to minimum controllable Cv (Kv).

■ **rapping**

knocking or jarring the pattern to loosen it from the sand in the mould before withdrawing the pattern.

■ **rare earth (re)**

any of a group of 15 similar metals with atomic numbers 57 to 71.

Also rare earth element, rare earth metal, lanthanide series, uncommon metals, Mischmetal.

■ **rare gases**

helium, argon, neon, krypton, xenon and radon.

■ **rat tail**

an expansion discontinuity in a sand casting, featured as a long, narrow, linear depression, resulting from sand expansion and minor buckling of the mould surface during filling of the mould.

■ **rate tools**

tools designed to be used repeatedly in a production setting to fabricate many parts rather than a single prototype or small number of demonstration parts.

■ **rationalised erosion rate**

in liquid impingement erosion, an erosion rate for impingement tests expressed in dimensionless form as follows: the volume of material lost per unit volume of (liquid or solid) particles impinging, both determined for the same area.

■ **reach**

the maximum distance from the centre line of the robo to the end of its tool mounting plate.

■ **reactive control**

a reactive control architecture tightly couples perception and action to produce efficient, real-time responses to the environment with little or no mediation of abstract representation.

■ **real area of contact**

in tribology, the sum of the local areas of contact between two solid surfaces, formed by contacting asperities, that transmit the interfacial force between the two surfaces. (Contrast with **apparent area of contact**).

■ **real-time operating systems**

real-time control tasks depend on the time at which sub-tasks complete. A real-time operating system controls the timing of computation and communication to guarantee that critical timing specifications are met.

■ **receiving ladle**

a ladle placed in front of the cupola into which all metal is tapped. It acts as a mixer and reservoir and to smooth out metal flow to the pouring area.

■ **recrystallisation**

a process whereby the distorted grain structure of cold-worked metals is replaced by a new, strain-free grain structure during annealing above a specific minimum temperature.

■ **recrystallisation temperature**

the lowest temperature at which the distorted grain structure of a cold-worked metal is replaced by a new, strain-free grain structure during prolonged annealing. Time, purity of the metal, and prior deformation are important factors.

■ **reduction**

the removal of oxygen or addition of hydrogen.

■ **redundant systems**

a system with more independently controlled variables than needed to solve a given task. Redundancy often involves the optimisation of secondary objective, as with kinematic conditioning.

■ **reference frame (rf)**

the state of motion of an observer. An inertial RF is a member of a set of all RFs moving uniformly with respect to one another, without relative acceleration. An RF is necessary but not sufficient to define a coordinate system (CS). A CS which requires an origin point and a oriented set of three orthogonal axes.

■ **reflectoscope**

an instrument for the ultrasonic testing of metals.

■ **refractory**

1) heat-resistant material, usually non-metallic, used for furnace linings etc., 2) the quality of resisting heat.

■ **refractory clay**

a clay which fuses at pce 25 (1590 °C, 2894 °F) or higher.

■ **regression analysis**

a statistical method of determining, or predicting, the value of a dependent variable, based on levels of one or more know independent variables.

■ **regrind**

previously moulded material reentering the processing cycle.

■ **reinforced plastics**

high strength fillers imbedded in the part.

■ **reinforcement**

key element added to the matrix to provide the required properties (primarily strength); ranges from short fibres through complex textile forms.

■ **reinforcement learning (rl)**

trial-and-error learning; RL algorithms solve optimal control problems using data gathered online and without requiring a dynamic model (although offline, model-based methods can be used as well).

■ **release agent**

used to prevent cured matrix material from bonding to tooling; usually sprayed or painted on mould.

■ **release agent (parting agent)**

a material, e.g. silicone, stearate, oil, or wax for lubricating a die pattern or core box to facilitate easy removal of a casting, mould or core.

■ **release film**

impermeable film layer that does not bond to the composite during cure.

■ **reliability**

the percentage of time during which the robot can be expected to be in normal operation. This is also known as the 'up time' of the robot.

■ **relief valve**

a self-operated, fast acting valve which is used to bleed off excessive pressure in a fluid system.

■ **remanence**

the remaining flux density after the magnetising force has been removed.

■ **remelt**

see **revert**.

■ **remotely operated**

operated or controlled from another place.

■ **removable bundle**

a type of heat exchanger in which the tube bundle can be removed from the shell pipe. The removable bundle provides easy cleaning of the shell side and also a less expensive way of replacing worn out tubes.

■ **repair welding**

any welding carried out after delivery to the end user, i.e., after the casting has been in service.

■ **repeatability**

the ability of the manipulator arm to position the end effecter at a particular location within a specified distance from its position during the previous cycle.

■ **repetitive impact erosion test**

in impingement erosion testing, an apparatus or method that produces a controlled or countable number of impacts by liquid or solid particles, of uniform size, shape, and impact velocity, all on the same location of the test specimen. One example of such a test is the "wheel-and-jet" type of liquid impact apparatus.

■ **replicast process**

a ceramic shell process similar to the investment casting process. Uses a pattern made from expanded polystyrene (EPS) and is surrounded by a thin ceramic shell.

■ **researcher**

a person who devotes themselves to research and study of a particular topic or field.

■ **reservoir**

a container used to store the liquid in a fluid power system.

■ **residual**

any element remaining in any alloy following melting and casting which was not added to meet an analytical specification limit.

■ **residual stress**

see **stress, residual**.

■ **resin**

solid polymeric material, often of high molecular weight, which exhibits a tendency to flow when subjected to stress, usually has a softening or melting range, and usually fractures conchoidally. As composite matrices, resins bind together reinforcement fibres.

■ **resin content**

see **matrix content**.

■ **resin transfer moulding (rtm)**

moulding process in which catalysed resin is transferred into an enclosed mould into which a fibrous reinforcement has been placed. The mould and/or resin may or may not be heated. RTM combines relatively low tooling and equipment costs with the ability to consolidate large structural parts.

■ **resin-rich**

filled with excess resin and thus departing from a consistent resin/fibre ratio.

■ **resin-starved**

lacking sufficient resin for fibre wetout.

■ **resistance**

an opposition to the flow of a fluid through a device or system. A measure of the effect of friction.

■ **resolved shear stress**

stress operating on a crystallographic slip system.

■ **resolver**

an electrical device used to measure the position of a shaft as it rotates.

■ **respirator**

a filtering device which covers the nose and mouth and prevents inhalation of dust or fumes for the specific contaminant being filtered out. Handkerchiefs and gauze masks give little or no protection.

■ **retaining ring assembly**

a metal assembly used on ACA, GC and/or OC packed joint heat exchangers. The retaining ring assembly performs the same job as a lantern ring. The retaining ring assembly eliminates the need for a stuffing box flange.

■ **reverse acting controller**

an air-operated controller in which the output pressure decreases as the controlled medium increases.

■ **reverse acting valve**

a valve that is normally closed and which requires an increase of fluid pressure or other mechanical means to open.

■ **reverse actuator**

the actuator in a reverse acting valve.

■ **reversing end**

the end of a heat exchanger where the tubeside fluid reverses its flow in a multi-pass unit. It usually contains only small vent and drain connections.

■ **revert**

recycled sprues, gates, risers, defective castings and machine chips.

■ **reynolds numbers**

used in hydraulics and in casting gating theory. A dimensionless value (dynamic viscosity / density) describing the fairly sudden shift of flow from laminar to turbulent. Re > 2000 represents turbulent flow. Laminar flow is seldom experienced in runner and gating systems.

■ **RF**

a reference frame (RF).

■ **rib**

a reinforcing section of the part.

■ **ribbon direction**

on a honeycomb core, the way the honeycomb can be separated. The direction of one continuous ribbon.

■ **ribbon flow**

a type of tube layout or pass rib pattern. It is used on our 8 inch BCF's and is so named because it creates an end to end flow which looks like a piece of ribbon candy.

■ **rigging**

gates, risers, loose pieces, etc., needed on the pattern to produce a sound casting.

■ **right-hand rule**

the right-hand rule is the standard convention for determining the sign of a rotation: point your right thumb into the positive rotation axis and curl your fingers into the forward rotational direction.

■ **rimmed steel**

a low-carbon steel.

■ **Ringelmann's scale**

in air pollution control, a black and white mesh scale reading from all clear to solid black, used to measure the density of smoke. Observer normally uses chart comparator 50 feet from the point where smoke emits.

■ **riser**

reservoir of molten metal from which casting feeds as it shrinks during solidification.

■ **riser distance**

the length of the riser neck. The term is applied to side risers only.

■ **riser height**

the distance from the top of the riser when liquid to the top of the riser neck. Riser height when sold is usually several inches less than when liquid because of contraction and loss of feed metal to the casting.

■ **riser neck**

the connecting passage between the riser and casting. Usually only the height and width or diameter of the riser neck are reported, although the shape can be equally important.

■ **riser pad (riser contact)**

an enlargement of the riser neck where it joins the casting. The purpose of the pad is to prevent the riser from breaking into the casting when it is struck or cut from the casting.

■ **riser, blind**

a riser that does not break through the top of the cope and is entirely surrounded by sand; opened to the atmosphere by means of a firecracker core.

■ **riser, open**

conventional form of riser usually located at the heaviest section of the casting and extending through the entire height of the cope.

■ **riser, side (side head)**

a riser attached to the side of a casting.

■ **riser, top (top head)**

a riser attached to the top surface of a casting.

■ **riser-gating**

practice of running metal for the casting through the riser to help directional solidification.

■ **rising stem**

a valve stem that turns and rises when the valve is open.

■ **robot**

a computer-operated, mechanical body that works on its own to do a variety of jobs. Robots can be programmed, and reprogrammed to move material, parts, tools, or specialised devices through various motions. Robots are not presently 'artificial people,' but helpful tools used in specific environments. For the time being, most robots could be considered computers with limbs, organs, tools, and other pieces of equipment attached. However, experiments in artificial intelligence are changing the definition of a robot in many ways for the future.

■ **robotic arm**

the limb of a robot that allows it to physically interact with other objects. A key function of the arm is to position the end-effector in the right place to do its job.

■ **robotics**

the study of problems associated with the design, application, control and sensory systems of robots.

■ **rockwell hardness**

See **hardness**.

■ **rodding**

reinforcing the sand in a core with metal rods or shapes to strengthen parts of the core.

■ **roi**

in economics, return on investment; profit from this particular source.

■ **rolling contact fatigue**

a damage process in a triboelement subjected to repeated rolling contact loads, involving the initiation and propagation of fatigue cracks in or under the contact surface, eventually culminating in surface pits or spalls.

■ **rolling over**

the operation of reversing the position of a flask. If the drag part of the pattern has been rammed with the parting surface downward, it is rolled over 180 degrees to allow core setting and placement of cope.

■ **rollover board**

a wood or metal plate on which the pattern is laid top face downward for ramming the drag half mould, the plate and half mould being turned over together before the joint is made.

■ **rollover machine**

a moulding machine with which the flask is rolled over before the pattern is drawn from the mould.

■ **rotational motion**

a degree of freedom that defines

motion of rotation about an axis.

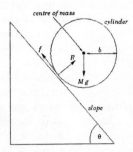

■ **roving**

large filament-count tow.

■ **RTM**

see **resin-transfer moulding**.

■ **Ru in**

in tribology, an initial transition process occurring in newly established wearing contacts, often accompanied by transients in coefficient of friction, or wear rate, or both, which are uncharacteristic of the given tribological system's long term Behaviour. (Synonym: break-in, wear-in.)

■ **run in**

in tribology, to apply a specified set of initial operating conditions to a tribological system in order to improve its long term frictional or wear Behaviour, or both. (See also Ru in, n.: Synonym: break in. and wear in.)

■ **runner**

a, channel through which molten metal or slag is passed from one receptacle to another; in a mould, the portion of the gate assembly that connects the downgate or sprue with the casting ingate or

riser. The term also applies to similar portions of master patterns, pattern dies, patterns, investment moulds and finished castings.

■ **runner balancing**

developing a runner system which delivers the required amount of melt to each cavity with the correct pressure to finish filling all the cavities simultaneously at the correct temperature for the part.

■ **runner design**

using the runner as a flow control device (positioning the gate and using the size of the runner to control the filling pattern within the cavity) in addition to getting the melt into the cavity.

■ **runner extension**

in a mould, that part of a runner which extends beyond the farthest ingate as a blind end. It acts as a dirt trap since the first rush of metal along the runner will pick up any loose particles of sand or dirt and carry them into the extension and not into the mould cavity.

■ **runner riser**

a conventional runner, usually in the horizontal plane, which permits flow of molten metal to the ingate and is large enough to act as a reservoir to feed the casting.

runners

channels cut interior to the mould which transport the melt from the entrance to the mould to the entrance to the cavity.

runout

a casting defect caused by incomplete filling of the mould due to molten metal draining or leaking out of some part of the mould cavity during pouring; escape of molten metal from a furnace, mould or melting crucible.

safety stuffing box packing

additional protection measures on bellows sealing designs.

sag

a decrease in metal section in casting due to sagging of the cope or core.

salamander

1. a heating device, usually of drum shape, in which fuel is burned in the open air by natural draft
2. iron which has collected in the bottom of a blast furnace during a blow.

salt bath

a bath of molten salts used for heating steels, for hardening or tempering.

sand

in metalcasting, a loose, granular material high in SiO_2, resulting from the disintegration of rock.

The name sand refers to the size of grain and not to mineral composition. Diameter of the individual grains can vary from approximately 6 to 270 mesh. Most foundry sands are made up principally of the mineral quartz (silica). Reason for this is that sand is plentiful, refractory, and cheap; miscellaneous sands include zircon, olivine, chromite, $CaCO_3$, black sand (lava grains), titanium minerals and others.

sand casting

metal castings produced in sand moulds.

sand control

procedure whereby various properties of foundry sand, such as fineness, permeability, green strength, moisture content, etc., are adjusted to obtain castings free from blows, scabs, veins, and similar defects.

sand mulling

a method of evenly distributing the bond around the sand grain by a rubbing action.

sand plow

a bladed device used to divert sand from a belt conveyor into a sand hopper.

sand porosity

volume of the pore spaces or folds in a sand. (Not synonymous with permeability).

sand reclamation

processing of used foundry sand grains by thermal, attraction or hydraulic methods so that it may be used in place of new sand without substantially changing current foundry sand practice.

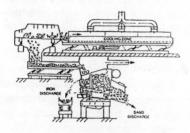

■ **sand tempering**

dampening and cutting over or otherwise mixing sand to produce uniform distribution of moisture, and allowing time for migration of water molecules.

■ **sand wall**

temporary independent wall separated from a slag pocket wall; facilitates slag removal and protects permanent wall.

■ **sandwich structure**

composite composed of lightweight core material (usually honeycomb or foam) to which two relatively thin, dense, high-strength, functional or decorative skins are adhered.

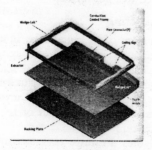

■ **sauter mean diameter, SMD [L]**

the diameter of a drop that has the same ratio of volume to surface area as the ratio of total volume to total surface area in a distribution of drops.

■ **scab**

an expansion discontinuity defect on the surface of a casting which appears as a rough, slightly raised surface blemish, crusted over by a thin porous layer of metal under which is a honeycomb or cavity that usually contains a layer of sand.

■ **scale space algorithms**

the space of causal, multi-scale representations of a signal constructed using blurring masks (typically gaussian kernels) of varying bandwidth. Each coarser version of the signal is obtained by filtering the finer version. In contrast to a multiresolution pyramid where each coarser version is subsampled, in the scale-space representation the resolution is preserved at all levels.

■ **scaling (scale)**

surface oxidation, partially adherent layers of corrosion products, left on metals by heating or casting in air or in other oxidising atmospheres.

■ **scanning electron microscope (SEM)**

an instrument used for obtaining microstructure images using an electron beam. The micrographs obtained give depth perception of the metal being observed.

■ **scarfing**

cutting off surface projections such as gates and risers from casting by means of gas torch.

■ **scavenging/vent air flushing**

the exhaust air of the positioner is picked up and used for ventilation of the spring chamber. This increases the working life of the actuators enormously, especially in high atmospheric humidity (e.g., in the tropics).

■ **SCFH**

standard cubic feet per hour.

■ **SCFM**

standard cubic feet per minute.

■ **schematic diagram**

a connected group of Mechanics blocks. An entire block diagram in a link model window has one or more schematics, each representing a distinct machine.

■ **scoring**

in tribology, a severe form of wear characterised by the formation of extensive grooves and scratches in the direction of sliding.

■ **scrap**

any output of a mould that is not usable as the primary product.

■ **scrap (metal)**

metal to be remelted; includes scrapped machinery fabricated items such as rail or structural steel and rejected castings.

■ **scratching**

in tribology, the mechanical removal or displacement, or both, of material from a surface by the action of abrasive particles or protuberances sliding across the surfaces. (See also **plowing**.)

■ **screen (sand)**

a sieve or riddle with openings of definite size used to separate one gain size from another or to remove lumps from sand.

■ **screen analysis (sieve analysis)**

distribution of particle size sand expressed in terms of the percentage of weight retained on each of a series of standard screens decreasing in mesh size and the percentage passed by the screen of finest mesh.

■ **screwed end**

a type of end fitting on a valve or other fluid component which is joined by threaded connections.

■ **scrim**

low-cost, woven reinforcing fabric in an open mesh construction.

■ **scrubbers**

see **wet scrubbers**.

■ **scuffing**

a form of wear occurring in inadequately lubricated tribosystems which is characterised by macroscopically-observable changes in surface texture, with features related to the direction of relative motion.

Notes: Features characteristic of

scuffing include scratches, plastic deformation, and transferred material. (Related terms: galling, scoring.)

■ **sealant**

paste or liquid applied to a joint that hardens in place to form a seal.

■ **sealed source**

any radioactive material that is encased in and is to be used in a container in a manner intended to prevent leakage of the radioactive material.

■ **seam**

a surface defect on a casting related to but of lesser degree than a cold shut; a ridge on the surface of a casting caused by a crack in the mould face.

■ **seat**

the part of a valve against which the closure element presses to effect a seal.

■ **secondary structure**

aerospace structure that is not critical to flight safety.

■ **segregated flow**

divided into three categories.

■ **segregation**

a concentration of alloying elements at specific regions, usually as a result of the primary crystallisation of one phase with the subsequent concentration of other elements in the remaining liquid.

■ **selenium**

a metalloid melting 220°C

(428°F) added to stainless steel to improve machinability.

■ **sensitivity**

the measure of the response of an instrument or control unit to a change in the incoming signal.

■ **sensor**

an input device that sends information about its surroundings and lets it know the exact position of the arm, or the state of the world around it. This information in the form of electronic signals, or data. Sensors can provide only limited feedback to the robot so it can do its job. Most robots of today are nearly deaf and blind, compared to the senses and abilities of even the simplest living things.

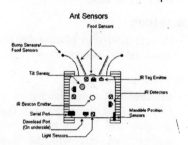

Ant Sensors

■ **separator**

a mechanical unit which separates or grades ground materials into constituent parts, used in the foundry to remove fines from the system sand and dust from the air.

■ **service factor**

a measure of the continuity of operation, generally expressed as the ratio of total running days for a given time period to the total calendar days in the period.

■ **servo controlled**

controlled by some type of servo component.

■ **servo lag**

the distance a robot arm will move after it has been commanded to stop.

■ **servo motor**

any type of motor that has controllable speed or position.

■ **servo valve**

a valve used to control the speed or position of another component by changing its flow.

■ **set point**

the target value which an automatic control device attempts to reach or to hold.

■ **setting**

the refractory insulation on the inside of the beater box.

■ **setting drawing**

the final assembly drawing of an ITT Standard heat exchanger. This drawing will always have a part number that starts with the number 5.

■ **s-glass**

denotes "structural glass" a magnesia/ alumina/ silicate glass reinforcement designed to provide very high tensile strength. Used in high-performance composites.

■ **shakeout**

1. the operation of removing castings from the mould
2. a mechanical unit for separating the moulding materials from

the solidified metal casting.

■ **shank**

the handle attached to a ladle.

■ **shaw (osborn-shaw) process**

a precision casting technique in ceramic moulds which do not require wax or plastic investment.

■ **shear**

a type of deformation in which parallel planes in the metal crystals slide so as to retain their parallel relation.

■ **shear modulus (g)**

in a torsion test, the ratio of the unit shear stress to the displacement caused by it per unit length in the elastic range. Units are Pa or psi.

■ **shear rate**

the rate at which a layer of melt slides over the layer below. Shear rate is velocity-related rather than force related.

■ **shear strain**

elastic displacement produced by pure shear loading.

■ **shear strength**

maximum shear stress a material is capable of withstanding without failure.

■ **shear stress**

the shearing force divided by the area. It is always a maximum at the outside of the flow channel. As it is force-related, it depends on the viscosity of the material, which in turn depends on the material and moulding conditions. The maximum allowable stress level is usually taken as 1% of the tensile strength of the material. High shear stress is unimportant at gates, and in sprues and runners.

■ **shelf life**

length of time in which a material can be stored and continue to meet specification requirements, remaining suitable for its intended use.

■ **shell assembly**

the name of the assembly into which the tube bundle fits. The shell also contains the shellside connections.

■ **shell head**

a shell head is a formed plate which is welded to the shell (or bonnet) pipe. The shell head can be many styles or shapes, including flanged and dished, elliptical, ellipsoidal, and hemispherical. Generally, as a head gets flatter it gets weaker, therefore designers can use a flat end plate or a thinner formed head to do the same job.

■ **shell moulding**

a process for forming a mould from resin-bonded sand mixtures brought in contact with pre-heated (300-500°F) metal patterns, resulting in a firm shell with a cavity corresponding to the outline of the pattern.

■ **shell side**

the side of a heat exchanger where the fluid circulates around the outside of the tubes.

■ **shewed tolerances**

tolerances which are non-symmetrically distributed about the design parameter.

■ **shield section**

the first two tube rows of the convection section. These tubes are exposed to direct radiation from the radiant section and usually receive about half of their heat in this manner.

■ **shift**

a casting defect caused by mismatch of cope and drag or of cores and mould.

■ **short shots**

sequential views of the flow front through the cavity.

■ **shortness (hot)**

brittleness in a metal at an elevated temperature.

■ **shotbalsting (shot peening)**

casting cleaning process employing a metal abrasive (grit or shot) propelled by centrifugal or air force.

■ **shoulder**

the manipulator arm link joint that is attached to the base.

■ **shrink**

the difference in volume between liquid metal and solid metal or the void (shrink hole) left in a casting because of it.

■ **shrinkage**

1) Liquid, contraction in volume as metal cools to solidification, 2) solidification, contraction in vol-

ume when the metal passes from the liquid to the sold at the freezing point (may expend over a range), 3) solid, the contraction on cooling from freezing point to normal temperature, 4) the decrease in dimension in clays occurring when drying at 100°C (212°F) and even more so on firing, 5) reduction in dimension of refractory material during heating.

■ **shrinkage cracks**

cracks that form in metal as result of the pulling apart of grains by contraction before complete solidification.

■ **shrinkage, patternmakers**

a linear scale or ruler, typically in inches or millimeters which has been lengthened by the percentage of linear shrinkage by which liquid metal contracts during solidification and cooling.

■ **sieve analysis**

see **screen analysis**.

■ **silica**

silicon dioxide, the prime ingredient of sand and acid refractories.

■ **silica brick**

refractory material of ganister, bonded with hydrated lime, and fired at high temperature.

■ **silica gel**

a colloidal form of silica used as a drying agent.

■ **silica sand**

sand with a minimum silica content of 95% used for forming casting moulds.

■ **silicon**

an abundant element, chemically classed as a non-metal, metallurgically a metal, used extensively in ferrous and non-ferrous alloys; melting point 1423°C (2593.4°F).

■ **silicon carbide fibre**

reinforcing fibre with high strength and modulus; density is equal to that of aluminium. May be formed as wires by chemical vapour deposition onto a carbon-filament core, or as filaments. Used in both organic and metal-matrix composites.

■ **simultaneous engineering**

refers to the process where user/ designer and producer interact to reduce lead time and improve the efficiency of a part. This process is faster and more efficient than the traditional sequential process of design and manufacture.

■ **single cavity mould**

produces one part with each cycle.

■ **single-impact damage**

see **damage**.

■ **sink marks**

an indentation on the surface of the part as a result of significant local change in wall section. The mark will occur in the thicker area.

■ **sintering**

the bonding of adjacent surfaces of particles of a mass of powder or a compact by heating to a suitable temperature and cooling.

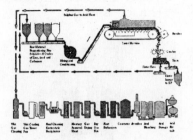

■ **sintering point**

that temperature at which the moulding material begins to adhere to the casting, or in a test when the sand coheres to a platinum ribbon under controlled conditions. Also, the temperature at which sand grains begin to adhere to one another.

■ **size**

material applied to textiles to facilitate subsequent operations such as weaving or braiding. Sizes may be used to bind together and stiffen warp yarns during weaving and/or to minimize abrasion and wear. Sizes are usually removed and replaced with finish before matrix application. Also called sizing.

■ **skim core (skimmer)**

a flat core or tile placed in a mould to skim a flowing stream of metal. Commonly used in pouring basins, it hold back slag and dirt while clean metal passes underneath to the downsprue.
See **core strainer**.

■ **skim gate**

a gating arrangement which

changes the direction of flow of molten metal and prevents the passage of slag and other undesirable materials into the mould cavity.

■ **skimming**

removing or hold back dirt or slag from the surface of the molten metal before or during pouring.

■ **skin**

a thin surface layer different chemically or structurally from the main mass of a metal object.

■ **skin-drying**

drying the surface of the mould by direct application of heat.

■ **SLA**

see **stereolithography apparatus**.

■ **slab core**

flat, plain core.

■ **slag inclusion**

nonmetallic solids entrapped in solid metal.

■ **slag trap**

an enlargement, dam, or extrusion in the gating or runners system in a mould for the purpose of preventing molten slag particles from entering the mould cavity.
See also **dirt trap**.

■ **slicking (sleeking)**

smoothing the surface of moulds.

■ **slide**

projection in the mould used to form the geometry of the part, which is not in the direction of the closing of the mould and must be withdrawn before the part can be ejected.

■ **sliding wear**

wear due to the relative motion in the tangential plane of contact between two solid bodies.

■ **slip casting**

in ceramics, a pouring slip, a water suspension of finely ground clay, into a plaster of paris mould. After it hardens it is dried and fired.

■ **slip-on flange**

a type of nozzle flange. A slip-on flange slips over the nozzle pipe and is welded in place.

■ **slug flow**

gas phase exists as large bubbles almost filling the pipe and separated by slugs of liquid , gas bubbles are rounded on their leading edge, fairly flat on trailing edge and are surrounded on their sides by a liquid film.

■ **slug**

see **liquid jet**.

■ **slurry**

a term loosely applied to any clay-like dispersion. It may be use to wash ladles or other refractory linings to impart a smooth surface; as a bonding addition to moulding sand; as a thin loam over specially made moulds or as a mixture to fine joints or cracks of a core, etc.

■ **smelting**

a metallurgical thermal process in which a metal is separated in fused

form from non-metallic materials or other undesired metals with which it is associated.

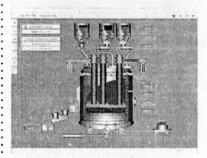

■ **smoke**

a type of emission resulting from incomplete combustion and consisting predominantly of small gas borne particles of combustible material present in sufficient quantity to be observable independently of the presence of other solids in the gas stream.

■ **soaking**

prolonged heating of a metal, furnace or ladle at a selected temperature.

■ **social behaviour**

the emotional, physical, and mental interactions between agents. This area includes a host of issues such as communication, interference, competition, cooperation, as well as collective and imitative learning.

■ **socket welded**

a valve or other fitting which slips over the end of a pipe and is made pressure tight by welding.

■ **sodium silicate**

see **water glass**.

■ soft tool

tool made of composites or a similar 'soft' material that is vulnerable to damage during use, storage or transportation.

■ softening

a process used to soften metals through annealing or tempering.

■ solid

that material which has a tendency to resist any attempt to change its size or shape.

■ soldering

1. joining metals by fusion of alloys that have relatively low melting points - most commonly, lead-based or tin-based alloys, which are the soft solders. Hard solders are alloys that have sliver, copper, or nickel bases, and use of these alloys with melting points higher than 800°F (426.7°C) is generally termed brazing.
2. the sticking or adhering of molten metal to portions of a die.

■ solenoid

an electrical coil with an iron section inside that will pull or push when current goes through the coil.

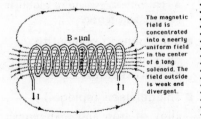

The magnetic field is concentrated into a nearly uniform field in the center of a long solenoid. The field outside is weak and divergent.

$B = \mu nI$

■ solid impingement erosion

progressive loss of original material from a solid surface due to continued exposure to impacts by solid particles. (Synonym: solid particle erosion, hard particle erosion.)

■ solid impingement

impingement by solid particles.

■ solid particle erosion

synonym for solid impingement erosion.

■ solidification

the physical process of change from a liquid to a solid state. See **casting analysis of solidification (13K)**.

■ solidification, shrinkage

the decrease in size accompanying the freezing of a molten metal.

■ solids loading ratio

see **particle concentration**.

■ solvent

liquid used to dissolve and clean materials.

■ sonar

the bouncing of sound waves and the measurement of their echo used to calculate distance.

■ sonic testing

using sound waves above audible frequency via a supersonic reflectoscope to measure time sound waves take returning from opposite sides of casting. Defects return the waves in more or less time.

■ **sorbite**

tempered martensite that has a micro-structure of distinctly granular appearance. Further tempering causes the appearance of clearly resolvable carbide particles (spheroidite).

■ **spacer**

a piece of tubing that slides over the tie rod or tie tube between the baffle plates. The spacer holds the baffle plate in a permanent position.

■ **spal process**

see **surface protection air liquide**.

■ **spalling**

in tribology, the separation of macroscopic particles from a surface in the form of flakes or chips, usually associated with rolling element bearings and gear teeth, but also resulting from impact events.

■ **spanning tree**

you obtain the spanning tree representation of a machine topology from the full machine topology by removing everything except bodies and joints and cutting each closed loop once.

■ **spary quenching**

after solution heat treating, a mode of quenching in which a spray of water is directed upon material just removed from the furnace.

■ **spec**

specification of the properties, characteristics, or requirements a particular material or part must have in order to be acceptable to a potential user of the material or part.

■ **specific gravity**

a numerical value representing the weight of a given substance as compared with the weight of an equal volume of water at 39°F (3.9°C), for which the specific gravity is taken as 1,000 kg/m³. See also **density**.

■ **specific heat**

equivalent to thermal capacity, or the quantity of heat required to produce a unit change in the temperature of a unit mass.

■ **specific volume**

volume of one gram of a substance at a specific temperature, usually 68°F (20°C).

■ **speed**

the maximum speed at which the end of the manipulator arm can move at a certain load.

■ **speed control**

valve used to meter flow and thus adjust actuating time, incorporates the use of an adjustable check valve which allows free flow in one direction and metered flow in the other.

■ **spheroidite**

a cementite aggregate of globular carbide and ferrite.

■ **spheroidised cementite**

the globular condition of iron carbide after a spheroidising treatment.

■ **spiegeleisen (spiegel)**

alloy of iron and manganese

used in basic and acid open hearth steel making practice. A high manganese pig iron, usually containing 15% or 20 Mn and 4.5-6.5% C.

■ **spiral test**

a method of interpreting the fluidity of an alloy by pouring molten metal into a mould with a long narrow channel. The length of such casting, under standardised conditions, is taken as the fluidity index of that alloy.

■ **splash core**

a core of tile placed in a mould to prevent erosion of the mould at places where metal impinges with more than normal force. Splash cores are commonly used at the bottom of large rammed pouring basins, at the bottom of long downsprues, or at the ingates of large moulds.

■ **splay**

area of abnormal racing of the melt in the mould causing surface blemish. Oil in the mould is one cause.

■ **spline**

general term used to describe the shaft with teeth cut in its parallel to the centreline of the shaft.

■ **spongy casting**

a casting in which the metal is porous and dendritic.

■ **spout**

a trough through which the metal flows from the furnace to the ladle.

■ **spring stroke**

the length a spring takes when uncompressed.

■ **sprue**

the entrance to the mould interior into which the melt is injected.

■ **sprue base**

an enlargement or rounded section at the bottom of the downsprue, used to help streamline the flow of metal into the runner, lowering the velocity.

■ **sprue bottom**

a print attached to the top or squeeze board of a mould to make an impression in the cope indicating where the sprue should be cut.

■ **sprue cutter**

a metal tool used in cutting the pouring aperture, the sprue hole.

■ **sprue hole**

the opening through which the metal is poured into the cope to run into the casting cavity.

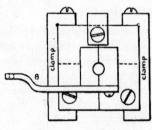

End View

■ **squeeze board**

a board used on the cope half of the mould to permit squeezing of the mould.

■ **squeeze head**

in certain type of moulding machines, a stationary or movable plate against which a filled mould is compressed, in order to complete the compacting of the sand.

■ **squeezer machine**

a power-operated, usually pneumatic, device used to pack sand into a flask.

■ **stabilising constraint**

numerically implements a constraint by modifying the dynamics of a system so that the constraint manifold is attractive, without changing the constrained solution. This constraint solver type is computationally the most efficient. The precision to which the constraint is maintained depends on scale or the physical system of units.

■ **stack**

a cylindrical steel, concrete, or brick shell, which carries flue gas to the atmosphere and provides necessary draft.

■ **stack effect**

the difference (buoyancy) between the weight of a column at high temperature gases inside the heater and/or stack and the weight of an equivalent column of external air, usually expressed in inches of water per foot of height.

■ **stack moulding**

see **multiple mould**.

■ **stack temperature**

the temperature of the flue gas as it leaves the convection section.

■ **stacking**

two or more heat exchangers which have been stacked together either side by side or one on top of the other. These units have interconnecting piping hooking them together.

■ **stacking sequence**

arrangement of ply orientations and material components in a laminate specified with respect to some reference direction.

■ **stainless steel**

a wide range of steels containing chromium or chromium and nickel, exhibiting high resistance to corrosion.

■ **standard deviation**

a statistical quantity used to describe the variation of a measurable attribute about some average value.

■ **standard pattern**

a pattern of high-grade material and workmanship in daily use or at frequent intervals. A pattern used as a master to make or check production patterns.

■ **standard samples**

a sample of know composition used to calibrate an instrument or method of analysis.

■ **standard shapes**

refractory units stocked by manufacturers or made from stock moulds.

■ **staple**

collection of short filaments of

spinnable length.

■ **static coefficient of friction**

the coefficient of friction corresponding to the maximum friction force that must be overcome to initiate macroscopic motion between two bodies.

■ **stationary tubesheet**

the tubesheet at one end of a removable bundle. It has a larger diameter than the floating tubesheet. The stationary tubesheet is held together in a permanent position between the bonnet and shell flanges.

■ **stave construction**

attaching staves to polygonshaped heads in the building of cylindrical bodies; also, standard method used in making semicircular core boxes.

■ **steam, dry**

steam with no water particles mixed in.

■ **steam, saturated**

steam in contact with liquid water at the boiling point.

■ **steel**

an alloy of iron and carbon that may contain other elements and in which the carbon content does not exceed about 1.7%; it must be malleable at some temperature while in the as-cast state.

■ **steels, sae**

common designation for the standard grades of steel approved by the Society of Automotive Engineers.

■ **steeped construction**

in patternmaking, the courses of material that when fastened together resemble steps.

■ **stepper motor**

a special electric motor that will rotate in steps of exact size.

■ **stereolithography apparatus (sla)**

equipment used for computerised building of three-dimensional models and patterns. Enables the data representation of a CAD solid model to be directly converted into a plastic model of a casting.

■ **sticker**

a lump on the surface of a casting caused by a portion of the mould face sticking to the pattern. Also, a forming tool used in moulding.

■ **stick-slip**

in tribology, a cyclic fluctuation in the magnitudes of friction force and relative velocity between two elements in sliding contact, usually associated with a relaxation oscillation dependent on elasticity in the tribosystem and on a decrease of the coefficient of friction with onset of sliding or with increase of sliding velocity.
Notes Classical or true stick-slip, in which each cycle consists of a stage of actual stick followed by a stage of overshoot "slip," requires that the kinetic coefficient of friction is lower than the static coefficient. A modified form of relaxation oscillation, with near-harmonic fluctuation

in motion, can occur when the kinetic coefficient of friction decreases gradually with increasing velocity within a certain velocity range. A third type of stick-slip can be due to spatial periodicity of the friction coefficient along the path of contact. Random variations in friction force measurements do not constitute stick-slip.

■ **stiction actuator**

applies discontinuous friction forces to a joint primitive according to the relative velocity of one body with the other body. If this relative velocity drops below a specified threshold, the relative motion ceases and the bodies or joints become locked rigidly to one another by static friction.
Above that threshold, the bodies or joints move relative to one another with kinetic friction.

■ **stiffness**

measure of the resistance of a material to deformation. The ratio of applied stress to resulting strain for a particular material.

■ **stock allowance**

material added to a part to allow for surface preparation or precise dimensioning by machining.

■ **stock core**

core of standard diameter usually made on a core machine and kept on hand, sawed to required length.

■ **stool**

support for a green sand core on a moulding machine.

■ **stool plate**

plate on a mould machine on which stools are mounted.

■ **stooling**

supporting green sand cores in machine moulding while pattern is being withdrawn.

■ **stopper head**

a refractory shape at the end of a stopper rod, usually clay and graphite, seated in a ladle's nozzle.

■ **stopper rod**

a device in a bottom-pour ladle for controlling the flow of metal through the nozzle into the casting. The stopper rod consists of a steel rod, protecting sleeves, and a graphite stopper head. It may also be a single piece manufactured from graphite.

■ **stopping-off**

filling in a portion of a mould cavity which is not to be cast.

■ **storage life**

amount of time a material can be stored and retain specific properties. (See also **shelf life**.)

■ **strain**

deformation resulting from applied stress. Measured as the change in length per unit of length in a given direction, and expressed in percentage or as inches per inch.

■ **strained casting**

a phrase used to describe the result when molten metal is poured into the mould at too fast a rate or under too great metallstatic pressure, causing the cope to rise slightly from the drag and resulting in an oversize casting.

■ **strainer**

a device through which a fluid is passed to remove insoluble materials.

■ **strainer core**

see **core strainer**.

■ **strand**

see **tow**.

■ **stratified smooth**

consists of liquid flowing along the bottom of the pipe and gas flowing along the top of the pipe with a smooth interface between the phases, it occurs at relatively low flow rates for both phases.

■ **stratified wavy**

occurs at higher rates of liquid and gas flow, where the interface becomes wavy.

■ **streamline flow**

steady flow of liquid without turbulence. Generally, not experienced in metalcasting.

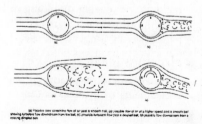

(A) Relative slow streaming flow of air past a smooth ball; (B) possible flow of air at a higher speed past a smooth ball; (C) probable turbulent flow past a dimpled ball; (D) possible flow downstream from a rotating dimpled ball.

■ **strength, retained**

compressive, shear, tensile, or transverse strength attained by a sand mixture after being subjected

to a cycle or cycles of heating and cooling which approximate foundry practice.

■ **strength, baked**

compressive, shear, tensile, or transverse strength of a moulded sand mixture when baked at a temperature above 230°F (110°C) and then cooled to room temperature.

■ **strength, compressive**

see **compressive strength**.

■ **strength, impact**

see **impact strength**.

■ **strength, shear**

see **shear strength**.

■ **strength, tensile**

see **tensile strength**.

■ **strength, yield**

see **yield strength**.

■ **stress**

internal resistance to change in size or shape, expressed in units of force (load) per unit area.

■ **stress concentration**

magnification of applied stress in the region of a notch, void, hole or inclusion.

■ **stress concentrators**

abrupt changes in geometry of the part serve as the focus of high stresses. Various means can be devised to relieve the abruptness of the geometric changes and thus the stresses.

■ **stress crack**

external or internal cracks in a composite caused by tensile stresses;

cracking may be present internally, externally or in combination.

■ **stress, relieving**

a heat treatment to reduce residual stresses followed by sufficiently slow cooling to minimize development of new residual stresses.

■ **stress, residual**

those stresses setup up in a metal as a result of non-uniform plastic deformation or the unequal cooling of a casting.

■ **stress-corrosion cracking**

spontaneous failure of metals by cracking under combined conditions of corrosion and stress, either residual or applied.

■ **STRI**

a classification system for robot controllers, based on the type of information input: Sequential, Tracking, Registration, Informational.

■ **strike-off**

operation of removing excess sand from top or core box or flask.

■ **stripper pins**

on certain moulding machines, a series of pins (usually four in number) which support the rammed flask-half at the parting surface so that the mounted pattern may be drawn by lowering.

■ **stripping**

removing the pattern from the mould or core box from core.

■ **stripping time**

in oil-oxygen and nobake mixture, the moment when the core box may be satisfactorily drawn from the core, or pattern from the sand.

■ **structural adhesive**

adhesive used to transfer loads between adherents.

■ **structural bond**

bond joining load-bearing components of an assembly.

■ **structural repair manual (srm)**

document prepared by an OEM that designates original structural materials (both composite and metal) used for a specific aircraft. It usually includes schematics for all parts and listings of fastener types and adhesives. It also suggests general repair methodology so that structural integrity can be maintained, including whether autoclave cure is required. Updated periodically by OEMs based on input from repair technicians.

■ **structural strength**

reduction in melt quality or distressed melt flow due to welding, melding, etc. during moulding reduce the structural integrity of the part, lowering longevity in use.

■ **structure (cast structure)**

the size and disposition of the constituents of a metal as cast.

■ **stub end**

a stub end is the fluid contact surface used with a lap-joint flange. At ITT Standard it is usually made of stainless steel but it can be other materials.

stud/stud bolt

a stud bolt is used to hold two or more pieces together. It is threaded the full length (T.F.L.) and fits through bolt holes which are not tapped. A hex nut is used on both ends. A stud is similar to studbolt except it threads into a tapped hole and a hex nut is used on one end only.

stuffing box flange

a flange used at a packed end joint. When a packed joint is tightened the packing ring is forced into this flange by the lantern ring or lantern gland.

styrofoam pattern

expendable pattern of foamed plastic, especially polystyrene, use in manufacturing casting by the Full mould process.

subcutaneous blowhole

blowholes at or near the surface of solidified metal, covered with a thin layer of metal. May also be called pinhole porosity.

subgate

entrance to the part from the runner located below the parting line. On ejection the part breaks away from the subgate.

submarine

a type of vehicle that can travel underwater.

submoulding

break up of a full moulding into component areas.

substrate

material upon the surface of which an adhesive-containing substance is spread for any purpose, such as bonding or coating.

subzero treatment

refrigeration of steel to promote transformation of retained austenite.

sulphur

a non-metallic element, melting point 444°C (831.2°F) occurring as an undesirable tramp (trace) element in most ferrous alloys.

sulphur prints

a macrographic method of examining for the distribution of sulphide impurities, in which a sheet of wet acidified bromide paper is placed on the polished surface to be examined.

superalloy

an alloy developed for very high temperature use where relatively high stresses are encountered and where oxidation resistance is needed.

supercooling

lowering the temperature of a molten metal below its liquidus during cooling.

superduty fireclay brick

having pce above 33 with less than 1.0 percent linear shrink in the 1599°C (2910°F) reheat test, and less than 4.0 percent loss in panel spalling test preheated at 1649°C (3000°F).

superheat

any increment of temperature above the melting point of a

metal; sometimes construed to be any increment of temperature above normal casting temperatures introduced for the purpose of refining, alloying or improving fluidity.

■ **superheated steam**

steam at any pressure which is heated to a temperature above the steam temperature at that pressure.

■ **supersaturated**

metastable solution in which the dissolved material exceeds the amount the solvent can hold in normal equilibrium at the temperature and under the other conditions that prevail.

■ **supersonic reflectoscope**

an instrument for sending, receiving, and measuring sound waves over 20,000 cycles per second.

■ **superstructure**

the part of a valve located above the body. It may include the stem, handle, bonnet and other parts.

■ **support foot**

a support foot is usually bolted to the heat exchanger using the bonnet to shell flange bolting.

■ **supramor**

an electromagnetic flaw detection ink for the rapid detection of subcutaneous and surface flaws in ferrous metals.

■ **surface appearance**

distressed melt flow due to welding, melding, splay, etc. will appear as surface imperfections.

■ **surface hardening**

conferring a superficial hardness to a steel while maintaining a relatively soft core.

■ **surface protection air liquide (SPAL)**

the use of liquid argon, liquid nitrogen, or carbon dioxide snow to minimize the reaction of air and molten metal that normally occurs in an induction furnace. The liquid or snow is fed onto the surface of the molten metal where it vapourises, displacing the air thus reducing slag and oxygen levels.

■ **surface texture**

the roughness, waviness, lay or other characteristics of the surface of a part.

■ **surface topography**

the geometrical detail of a solid surface, relating particularly to microscopic variations in height.

■ **surfacing**

depositing a filer metal on a metal surface by any method to obtain certain desired properties or dimensions.

■ **swell**

a casting defect consisting of an increase in metal section due to the displacement of sand by metal pressure.

■ **swing**

the rotation about the centre line of the robot.

■ **swing frame grinder**

a device for grinding large castings where the work remains stationary. This grinder, too large to be hand lifted, is usually suspended from a hoist.

■ **symmetric laminate**

laminate in which the stacking sequence for the plies located on one side of the geometric midplane are the mirror image of the stacking sequence on the other side of the midplane.

■ **synthetic moulding sand**

any sand compounded from selected individual materials which, when mixed together, produce a mixture of the proper physical and mechanical properties from which to make foundry moulds.

■ **system sand**

foundry sand used in making moulds and which eventually becomes the bulk of the sand used in the mechanical system or mechanized unit.

■ **tabgate**

edge-gating or sub-gating into a tab added to the part for gating purposes only.

■ **tachometer**

a device used to measure the speed of a rotating shaft.

■ **tack**

stickiness of an uncured prepreg.

■ **tactile sensor**

a sensor that detects the presence of an object or measures force or torque through contact with the object.

■ **Takens' theorem**

the result that hidden state of a multi-dimensional dynamical system can be reconstructed from measurements of a scalar variable.

■ **tape**

thin unidirectional prepreg in widths up to 12 inches for carbon fibre.

■ **TCP**

abbreviation for tool centre point. An artificial point in space relative to the robot arm where the centre of end-of-arm tooling will be.

■ **teaching**

the process of programming a robot to perform a desired sequence of tasks.

■ **tee**

a three-port fitting used to join one pipe at right angles to two other pipes.

■ **teleoperation**

human operation of a machine across some barrier, traditionally large distances. Teleoperation often implies some degree of machine autonomy although most systems rely exclusively on human inputs in the robot's configuration space.

■ **TEMA**

Tubular Exchange Manufacturer's Association. The TEMA Standards cover the design, manufacture, installation, operation, and maintenance of shell and tube heat exchangers. TEMA C is for generally moderate requirements of commercial and general process requirements. TEMA B is for chemical process services. TEMA R generally serves requirements of petroleum and related processing applications.

■ **temper**

1. reheating hardened, normalised or mechanically worked steel to a temperature below the critical range to soften it and improve impact strength.
2. the moisture content of a sand at which any certain physical test value is obtained, i.e., temper with respect to green compressive strength, permeability, retained compressive strength, etc.
3. to mix material with enough liquid to develop desired moulding properties.

■ **temper brittleness**

brittleness that results when certain steels are held within or cooled slowly through a certain range of temperature below the transformation range. The brittleness is revealed by notched-bar impact tests at room temperature or lower temperatures.

■ **temper stressing**

quenching in water from the tempering temperature to improve fatigue strength.

■ **temperature**

degree of warmth or coldness in relation to an arbitrary zero measured on one or more of accepted scales, as Centigrade, Fahrenheit, etc.

■ **temperature, holding**

1. temperature above the critical phase transformation range at which castings are held as a part of the heat treatment cycle
2. the temperature maintained when metal is held in a furnace, usually prior to pouring.

■ **temperature, pouring**

the temperature of the metal as it is poured into the mould.

■ **tempered martensite**

martensite that has been heated to produce to BCC iron and a fine dispersion of iron carbide.

■ **tensile strength**

the maximum stress in uniaxial tension testing which a material will withstand prior to fracture. The ultimate tensile strength is calculated from the maximum load applied during the test divided by the original cross-sectional area.

■ **terminal erosion rate**

in cavitation or liquid impingement erosion, the final steady-state erosion rate that is reached (or appears to be approached asymptotically) after the erosion rate has declined from its maximum value. (See also **terminal period and erosion rate-time pattern.**)

■ **terminal period**

in cavitation or liquid impingement erosion, a stage following the deceleration period, during which the erosion rate has leveled off and remains approximately constant (sometimes with superimposed fluctuations) at a value substantially lower than the maximum rate attained earlier. This occurs in some, but not all, cavitation and liquid impingement tests. (See also **erosion rate-time pattern**.)

■ **ternary alloy**

an alloy that contains three principal elements.

■ **test lug**

an ear like projection cast as part of the casting and later removed for testing purposes.

■ **test pressure**

generally 1.5 times the design pressure. The pressure used during a hydrostatic test. The test is made to detect leaks at any joint on the heat exchanger.

■ **tg**

glass-transition temperature.

■ **thermal conductivity**

the property of matter by which heat energy is transmitted through particles in contact. For engineering purposes, the amount of heat conducted through refractories is usually given in Btu per hour for one square foot of area, for a temperature difference of one degree Fahrenheit, and for a thickness of one inch, Btu/hr ·ft ·F/in.

■ **thermal contraction**

the decrease in a linear dimension and volume of a material accompanying a change of temperature.

■ **thermal degradation**

deterioration of the material by heat, characterised by molecular scission.

■ **thermal expansion**

the increase in a linear dimension and volume of a material accompanying a change of temperature.

■ **thermal fatigue**

failure resulting from rapid cycles of alternate heating and cooling.

■ **thermal shock**

stress developed by rapid and uneven heating of a material.

■ **thermal shut-off**

material freezes causing blockage.

■ **thermal spalling**

breaking up of refractory from stresses which arise during repeated heating and cooling.

■ **thermal stability**

resistance of a material to drastic changes in temperature.

■ **thermal stress cracking**

crazing and cracking of some thermoplastic resins from overexposure to elevated temperatures.

■ **thermocouple**

a device for measuring temperatures by the use of two dissimilar metals in contact; the junction of these metals gives rise to a measurable electrical potential which varies with the temperature of the junction. Thermocouples are used to operate temperature indicators or heat controls.

■ **thermography**

the technique of obtaining a photographic record of heat distribution in a solid or fluid.

■ **thermoplastic**

class of plastics that can be repeatedly softened by heating and hardened by cooling through a temperature range characteristic of the plastic, and that in the softened state can be shaped by flow into articles by moulding or extrusion.

■ **thermoset**

class of plastics that, when cured using heat, chemical or other means, changes into a substantially infusible and insoluble material. Once cured, a thermoset cannot be returned to the uncured state.

■ **thickness**

depth of the material and contributory to pressure requirements; thickening reduces the pressure required to fill the part.

■ **thixotropic**

substance that is gel-like at rest, but fluid when agitated, and thus can be applied easily but clings to a vertical surface. Thixotropic substances have high static shear strength and low dynamic shear strength at the same time, and lose viscosity under stress.

■ **three-way pilot valve**

a pilot valve used with single acting (spring-return) actuators.

■ **throttling**

the regulation of flow through a valve or other device.

■ **thrust**

a force exerted on an object which causes a linear movement.

■ **tie bar, rod**

bar or rod-shaped part of the casting added to prevent distortion caused by uneven contraction between separated members.

■ **tie rod**

a small diameter rod which threads into the stationary end tubesheet. This rod ties the baffles and spacers together.

■ **tie tube**

a tie tube takes the place of the tie rod in a small diameter heat exchanger. It serves the same purpose as a tie rod.

■ **tight flask**

a type of flask which remains on mould during pouring. Lugs are normally provided for clamping cope and drag together for pouring.

■ **time scan**

effects of mould and melt temperature and injection time changes on pressure, stress and temperature at the end of flow.

■ **titanium**

a white metallic element, melting point 1660°C (3020°F), having a high strength-to-weight ratio; useful in aircraft parts.

■ **tolerance**

the permissible deviation of a dimension from the nominal or desired value. Minimum clearance between mating parts.

■ **tolerancing constraint**

a tolerancing constraint is numerically implemented on constrained degrees of freedom only up to a specified accuracy and/or precision. This accuracy/precision is independent of any accuracy/precision limits on the solver used to integrate the system's motion, although constraints cannot be maintained to greater accuracy than the accuracy of the solver. The precision to which the constraint is maintained depends on scale or the physical system of units. Tolerancing constraints are useful in realistic simulation of slippage ('slop' or 'play') in constraints.

■ **tool**

the mould, either one- or two-sided and either open or closed, in or upon which composite material is placed in order to make a part.

■ **tool steel**

any high-carbon or alloy steel used to make a cutting tool for machining metals and for metal-casting dies.

■ **tooling points**

the fixed positions on the casting surfaces used for references during layout and machining.

■ **tooling resins**

plastic resins, chiefly epoxy and silicone, that are used as tooling aids.

■ **top-and-bottom guided**

a type of valve design in which the plug is aligned by guides in the valve body or in the bonnet and bottom flange.

■ **topology**

the global connectivity of the ele-

ments of a machine. For mechanical models, the elements are bodies and the connections are joints, constraints, and drivers. Two topologies are equivalent if you can transform one system into another by continuous deformations and without cutting connections or joining elements.

An open system has no closed loops.

An open chain is topologically equivalent to a line; and each body is connected to only two other bodies, if the body is internal, or one other body if it is at an end. An open tree has one or more branch points. A branch point is where an internal body is connected to more than two other bodies. A tree can be disconnected into multiple chains by cutting at the branch points.

A closed loop system has one or more closed loops. The number of closed loops is equal to the minimum number of joints, minus one, that must be cut to dissociate a system into two disconnected systems.

An actual system can have one of these primitive topologies or can be built up from multiple primitive topologies.

■ **touch sensor**

a sensor that detects the presence of an object by coming into contact with it.

■ **toughness**

the ability of the metal to absorb energy and to deform plastically during fracture. Toughness values obtained in testing depend upon the test temperature, the rate of loading, the size of the test specimen, as well as the presence of a notch and its acuity.

■ tow

continuous, ordered assembly of essentially parallel, collimated filaments, normally continuous filaments without twist. Same as strand.

■ tow size

designation indicating the number of filaments in a tow, usually a number followed by K, indicating multiplication by 1,000 (for example, 12K tow has 12,000 filaments).

■ tower oven

vertical, continuous core oven with suspended shelves attached to sprocket-driven chains.

■ tracking system

a set of rails on which a robot can travel from one place to another.

■ tramp element (trace)

contaminant in the components of a furnace charge, or in the molten metal or casting, whose presence is felt to be either unimportant or undesirable to the quality of the casting.

■ transducer

an element used to convert one form of energy into another, e.g., pressure into electrical voltage.

■ transfer ladle

a ladle that may be supported on a monorail or carried in a shank and used to transfer metal from the melting furnace to the holding furnace or from furnace to pouring ladles.

■ transformation (temperature) range

the critical temperature at which a change in phase occurs. To distinguish between the critical points in heating and cooling those in heating are referred to as the Ac points (c for Chauffage or heating) and those in cooling, Ar. (r for Refroidissement).

■ transition flow

liquid slugs between the gas bubbles essentially disappear, and at some point the liquid phase becomes discontinuous and gas phase becomes continuous.

■ triaxial fabric

fabric with three non-interwoven layers.
+45°,45° and either 0° or 90° which are bonded together, usually by through-the-thickness stitching, to form a single sheet of fabric. (See also **biaxial fabric, quadraxial fabric**.)

■ triboelement

one of two or more solid bodies which comprise a sliding, rolling or abrasive contact, or a body subjected to impingement or cavitation. (Each triboelement contains one or more tribosurfaces.)
Notes Contacting triboelements may be in direct contact, or may be separated by an intervening lubricant, oxide, or other film that affects tribological interactions between them.

■ tribology

the science and technology concerned with interacting surfaces in relative motion, including friction, lubrication, wear, and erosion.

■ tribosurface

any surface (of a solid body) that is in moving contact with another surface or is subjected to impingement or cavitation.

■ tribosystem

any system that contains one or more triboelements, including all mechanical, chemical and environmental factors relevant to tribological behaviour. (See also **triboelement.**)

■ trigger point

the exact point at which a component will change from one state to another.

■ tube guide

device used to direct movement of tubes in one particular direction.

■ tube layout

the tube layout drawing shows the positioning of the tubes inside the heat exchanger. It also shows the locations of the tierods.

■ tube sheet

a large tube support plate located in the convection section and supports a number of tubes. The end supports are usually carbon steel or low-alloy steel and make up one side of the header box. The inside of the end supports, which is exposed to the flue gas, is insulated. Intermediate supports are exposed to flue gas on both sides and are fabricated of suitable alloy material.

■ tube side

the side of a heat exchanger where the fluid circulates through the inside of the tubes. See Shell Side.

■ tube support

a metal device, which supports the weight of the tube.

■ tubesheet

the tubesheet is a plate that secures both ends of the tube in a heat exchanger. Both the shellside and tubeside mediums come in contact with it.

■ tungsten

steel-gray, metallic element, mp 3380°C (6116°F) used for electric lamp filament, x-ray tube target, and as alloy element in high-speed steels.

■ turbulent flow

characterised by a mixing action throughout the flow field, and the mixing is caused by eddies of varying size within the flow.

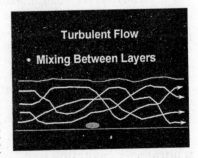

Turbulent Flow

• Mixing Between Layers

■ turndown

reduced operating conditions

compared to design conditions. This usually refers to reduced heat duty, which may be the result of reduced throughout and/or reduced enthalpy requirements.

■ **turntable**

the base on which a centrifugal casting mould rests.

■ **twist**

measure of the number of turns per unit length that a fibre bundle makes around its axis. "Z"-twist denotes a right-handed twist, while "S"-twist denotes a left-handed twist. "U" is often used to represent no twist and "N" means never twisted.

■ **two-side fired tubes**

radiant section tubes which are exposed on both sides to direct radiation from the burners.

■ **ultimate resilience**

R_u [FL^{-2}],
a material parameter defined by the equation:
$R_u = S_u^2/2E$
where:
S_u = ultimate tensile strength, and.
E = elastic modulus, as determined from a conventional tension test. Notes This parameter has been suggested as a criterion of erosion resistance. A modification of this, the true ultimate resilience, may be defined as [S_u /(1 R_a /100)]^2/ 2E, where R_a = reduction of area, %, in the tension test.

■ **ultrasonic cavitation test device**

a vibratory cavitation test device

whose driving frequency is in the ultrasonic range, about 20 kHz or greater. (For lower frequencies, the term vibratory cavitation test device is preferred.)

■ **ultrasonic cleaning**

immersion cleaning aided by ultrasonic waves which cause microagitation.

■ **ultrasonic testing**

a non-destructive method of testing metal for flaws based on the fact that ultrasonic waves are reflected and refracted at the boundaries of a solid medium.

■ **undercooling**

see **supercooling**.

■ **undercut**

a protuberance or indentation that impedes withdrawal from a mould.

■ **underflow**

the dominant flow of two confronting flows, over the other. The lesser flow reverses direction giving poor surface appearance and structural strength. Underflow should be avoided by positioning gates so that the flow fronts meet at the end of filling.

■ **unidirectional**

referring to fibres that are oriented in the same direction, such as unidirectional fabric, tape or laminate.

■ **unidirectional flow pattern**

plastic flowing in one direction with a straight flow front throughout filling.

■ **uniform cooling time**

cooling time the same throughout the part to avoid warping.

■ **unkilled steel**

a wild steel insufficiently deoxidised so that it evolves gas and blowholes during solidification.

■ **upgrading**

in castings, the removal and repair of discontinuities to raise the quality level of the casting beyond that which can be economically achieved by good foundry practice.

■ **upper yield point (also yield point)**

denoted in yield point phenomenon as a distinct break from the elastic region accompanied by a drop in load, yet prior to plastic deformation in the stress-strain curve in a low-carbon steel.

■ **urea formaldehyde resin**

a thermosetting product of condensation from urea or thio-urea and formaldehyde, soluble in water and used as a sand binder in core and mould compounds.

■ **vacuum**

a region in which the air pressure is less than atmospheric pressure.

■ **vacuum casting**

a casting in which metal is melted and poured under very low atmospheric pressure; a form of permanent mould casting where the mould is inserted into liquid metal, vacuum is applied, and metal drawn up into the cavity.

■ **vacuum degassing**

the use of a vacuum technique to remove dissolved gases from molten alloys.

■ **vacuum refining**

melting in a vacuum, usually by electrical induction, to remove gaseous contaminants from the metal.

■ **vacuum-bag moulding**

moulding technique wherein the part is cured inside a layer of film from which entrapped air is removed by vacuum.

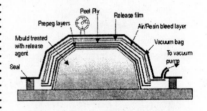

■ **value analysis**

in manufacturing, an analysis to determine the most economical method of manufacturing, taking into account the cost and the process capability of alternate manufacturing systems under consideration, their degree of variation, the benefits of the resultant product, and desired quality and production quantity and rate.

■ **valve**

a device for regulating the flow of fluid into something else.

■ **valve body**

the main part of a valve. It contains the passages for the flow medium, seating surfaces and inlet and outlet fittings.

valve plug

the part of a valve which moves to restrict the area through which the fluid travels.

valve trim

the internal components of a valve which are exposed to the flowing fluid.

valve, flow control

a valve used to control the rate of fluid flow.

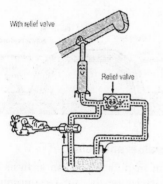

With relief valve

Relief valve

valve, pilot

a valve used to operate another valve.

valve, pressure reducing

a valve used to limit the outlet pressure from a source.

valve, shutoff

a valve designed to operate fully open or fully closed, but not at an intermediate position.

vanadium

a white, hard, metallic element, mp 1800°C (3272°F), used as an alloy in iron and steel; a powerful carbide stabiliser and deoxidiser.

vegetable oils

oils extracted from plants, used as drying oils in oil core manufacture. Linseed oil is an example.

veins

a discontinuity on the surface of a casting appearing as a raised, narrow, linear ridge that forms upon cracking of the sand mould or core due to expansion of the sand during filling of the mould with molten metal.

velocity

the rate of change of position with time. Common units are meters per second (SI metric) and feet per second (British).

venting

perforation with a vent wire of the sand over and around a mould cavity to assist in the escape of the gases.

vertical axis casting machine

a centrifugal casting machine in which the axis of rotation of the mould is vertical.

vertical stroke

the amount of vertical motion of a robot arm from one elevation to the other.

vibratory cavitation test device

a device used to generate cavitation in a liquid through the vibrations of a solid surface in contact

with the liquid. Usually such devices are driven at a frequency roughly in the range from 10 to 30 kHz by a magnetostrictive or a piezoelectric transducer.
Notes-Vibratory cavitation erosion test devices can be divided into two classes, according to whether the specimen itself is the vibrating body and generates cavitation adjacent to its surface, or whether the specimen is held stationary and cavitation is induced by other vibrating surfaces. Unless otherwise specified, the former is generally implied.

■ **vibratory cavitation**

cavitation caused by the pressure fluctuations within a liquid, induced by the vibration of a solid surface immersed in the liquid.

■ **vicat softening point**

the temperature at which a flat ended needle will penetrate a specimen under a specified load using a uniform rate of temperature rise.

■ **vicers diamond pyramid hardness tester**

patented indentation hardness machine. See **hardness**.

■ **virbrator**

a device, operated by compressed air of electricity, for loosening and withdrawing patterns from a mould, or for vibrating a hopper or chute to promote the flow of material from the hopper or chute.

■ **virgin material**

never processed other than that

required for initial pellet manufacture.

■ **virgin metal (primary metal)**

metal extracted directly from the ore; not previously used.

■ **virtual and augmented reality**

the use of computer generated sensory feedback, usually visual displays, to alter the perceived environment of a human user. This environment can be largely computer generated (virtual) or else a computer enhancement of the real world (augmented).

■ **viscosity**

the resistance of fluid substance to flowing, quantitatively characteristic for an individual substance at a given temperature and under other definite external conditions.

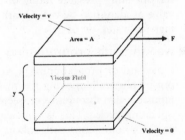

■ **vision sensor**

a sensor that identifies the shapes, location, orientation, or dimensions of an object through visual feedback, such as a television camera.

■ **void**

an unfilled space within a solid

material.

■ volatiles

materials, such as water and alcohol, in a sizing or resin formulation that can be vapourized at room or slightly elevated temperatures.

■ volume concentration

see **particle concentration**.

■ VRML

Virtual Reality Modeling Language, an open, Web-oriented ISO standard for defining three-dimensional virtual worlds in multimedia and the Internet. The Virtual Reality Toolbox uses VRML to create and populate virtual worlds with user-defined bodies.
In VRML, body rotations are represented in the axis-angle form.

■ W.O.G. rating

the operating pressure rating of a valve as identified by valve markings for water, oil or gas.

■ walkthrough programming

a method of programming a robot by physically moving the manipulator arm through a complete operating cycle. This is typically used for continuous path robots.

■ warp

fibre bundles in a woven fabric that run parallel to the length of the loom, lengthwise along the long-dimension of the fabric.

■ warpage

deformation other than contraction that develops in a casting between solidification and room temperature; also, distortion occurring during annealing, stress relieving, and high-temperature service.

■ warping

acquired contortion of the part due to differential shrinking of the material.

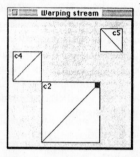

■ wash

a casting defect resulting from erosion of sand by metal flowing over the mould or corded surfaces. They appear as rough spots and excess metal on the casting surface. Also call cuts.

■ washburn core

a thin core which constricts the riser at the point of attachment to the casting. The thin core heats quickly and promotes feeding of the casting. Riser removal cost is minimised.

■ water absorption

ratio of weight of water absorbed by a material to the weight of dry material.

■ water box

see bonnet assembly and channel assembly. Another name for bonnet or channel.

■ **water glass**

sodium silicate (an inorganic binder system), a viscous liquid which when mixed with powered fireclay forms a refractory cement.

■ **water hammer**

vibration in a fluid system due to a rapid decrease in the velocity of a liquid from closing a valve.

■ **water jet**

high-pressure water stream used for cutting polymer composite parts.

■ **water test**

to subject a casting to water pressure in such a manner that any porous areas will show leakage.

■ **wax pattern**

1. a precise duplicate, allowing for shrinkage, of the casting and required gates, usually formed by pouring or injecting molten wax into a die or mould
2. wax moulded around the parts to be welded by a termite welding process.

■ **wear map**

a calculated or experimentally determined diagram that identifies regions within each of which the wear mechanism or wear rate remains substantially the same, the regions being separated by transition lines or bands that are functions of two or more parameters.
Notes:
1. Wear maps may be of two types: wear mechanism maps or wear rate maps. The first identi-fies regions within which the wear mechanism remains the same, and the transition between regions may or may not involve a step change in wear rate. The second identifies regions of substantially constant wear rate, wherein it is to be understood that transitions should involve a change in wear rate of at least a factor of ten.
2. Usually, in two-dimensional diagrams, the coordinate parameters are load (in terms of force or contact pressure) and sliding velocity, possibly made no dimensional by some normalising procedure. However, these may be replaced by other parameters, for example temperature, or (for fretting wear) amplitude.

■ **wear mechanism map**

see **wear map**.

■ **wear rate map**

see **wear map**.

■ **wear rate**

the rate of material removal or dimensional change due to wear per unit of exposure parameter, for example, quantity of material removed (massolume, thickness) in unit distance of sliding or unit time.
Notes: Because of the possibility of confusion, the manner of computing wear rate should always be carefully specified. (See also **erosion rate**.)

■ **wear**

damage to a solid surface, generally involving progressive loss of material, due to relative motion between that surface and a contacting substance or sub-stances.

wearable computing

the design and use of general-purpose computing devices that interfere relatively little with an individual's daily activities. 'Wearables' offer a flexible and efficient means for controlling and visualising the Behaviour of complex systems.

wear-in

see *Ru in.*

weave

fabric pattern formed from interlacing yarns. In plain weave, warp and fill fibres alternate to make both fabric faces identical. A satin weave pattern is produced by a warp tow over several fill tows and under one fill tow (for example, eight-harness satin would have one warp tow over seven fill tows and under the eighth).

weft

see **fill.**

weld bead

the built-up portion of a fusion weld, formed either from the filler metal or the melting of the parent metal.

weld line

the intersection of two confronting flow fronts creating areas of local weakness. Weld lines should be positioned in the least sensitive areas.

weld neck flange

a type of nozzle flange. A weld neck flange is used when a butt weld is required. This means the end of the flange butts up against a piece of pipe, both the flange and the pipe are bevelled. The joint provides sound weld with no overlapping of parts.

welding

a process used to join metals by the application of heat. Fusion welding, which includes gas, arc, and resistance welding, requires that the parent metals be melted.

welding electrode

a metal or alloy in rod or wire forms used in electric arc welding to maintain the arc and at the same time supply molten metal or alloy at the point where the weld is to be accomplished.

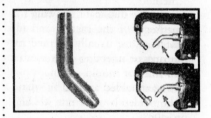

welding flash

skin exposed too long to the ultraviolet rays of welding or melting arcs will burn as in a sunburn. Though temporary blindness can result, it is not permanent, as is popularly believed.

welding shielded-arc

electric-arc welding in which the molten weld metal is protected from the atmosphere. An inert gaseous atmosphere or fluxcoated electrode may be employed.

welding stress

that stress resulting from localised heating and cooling of metal during welding.

welding

in tribology, the bonding between metallic surfaces in direct contact, at any temperature.

welding, arc

welding accomplished by using an electric arc that can be formed between a metal or carbon electrode and the metal being welded; between two separate electrodes, as in atomic hydrogen welding or between the two separate pieces being welded, as in flash welding.

welding, autogenous

method of uniting two pieces of metal by melting their edges together without solder or any added welding metal, as by the thermite process that employs a medium of finely divided aluminium powder and oxide or iron by which a temperature of some 2982.2°C (5400°F) is obtained.

wet layup

application of a resin to a dry reinforcement in the mould.

wet scrubber (gas washer)

in air pollution control, a liquid (usually water) spray device for collecting pollutants in escaping foundry gases.

wet winding

filament winding wherein fibre strands are impregnated with resin

immediately before contact with the mandrel.

wetout

saturation with resin of all voids between strands and filaments.

wetting agent

surface-active agent that promotes wetting by decreasing the cohesion within a liquid.

Widmanstatten structure

plate-like structure seen in grains of steel in the course of transformation of a solid solution.

wild steel

steel which has not been completely deoxidised and reacts violently after casting due to liberation of gases of cooling.

wind angle

measure in degrees between the direction parallel to the filaments and an established reference point.

winding

process in which continuous material is applied under controlled tension to a form in a predetermined geometric relationship to make a structure. A matrix material to bind the fibres together may be added before, during or after winding. Filament winding is the most common type.

winding pattern

in filament winding, recurring pattern of the filament path after a certain number of mandrel revolutions.

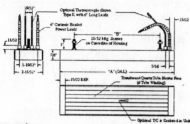

wire

large diameter (greater than about 2 mils) high-performance fibre, such as boron or silicon carbide, usually made by chemical vapour deposition onto a filamentary substrate.

wire drawing

the erosion of a valve seat under high velocity flow whereby thin wire-like gullies are eroded away.

wire mesh

fine wire screen used to dissipate the electrical charge from lighting.

woof

same as fill.

work cell

a group of machines all working together on a common part and physically located together.

work envelope

all of the places a single robot can reach in its surroundings, within its range of motion. The work envelope of each robot is suited to the job it is programmed to accomplish, and can vary considerably from one robot to another.

work in progress

an accounting term used to express the value of material taken up continuously by the work process.

work station

a stationary position where work is performed, the work piece moving to the station.

woven roving

heavy, coarse fabric produced by weaving continuous roving bundles.

wrench closure

the property of an arrangement of contacts, usually from a robotic hand or a fixturing device, that guarantees that the contact system can reject disturbance forces on the object (up to limitations in the manipulator). Wrench closure asserts that there exists a set of contact forces and moments that surrounds and contains the origin in the six dimensional wrench space. The analysis involves estimating the set of forces that can be transmitted by contacts and can include frictional forces in the contact model.

wrinkle

imperfection in the surface of a laminate that looks like a crease in one of the outer layers. This occurs in vacuum-bag moulding when the bag is improperly placed.

wrist

the manipulator arm joint to which an end effecter is attached.

x-axis

usually, the axis in the plane of the laminate used as 0° reference. Typically, the y-axis is the axis in the plane of the laminate perpen-